New Practice in Music Theory

by Josephine Koh

Grade 3

Based on the new theory syllabus of the Associated Board of the Royal Schools of Music.

Published by
Yamaha Music (Asia) Pte Ltd
140 Paya Lebar Road
#03-11, A-Z Building
Singapore 409015

2nd Edition 1994, 1999
Reprinted 1995, 1996, 1997, 1999, 2000, 2002, 2003, 2004
ISBN 981-3012-32-3

3rd Edition September 2005
Reprinted 2006

Cover design by Lee Kowling

for Wholesales Enquiries, please write to:
YAMAHA MUSIC (ASIA) PTE LTD
(Co. Reg. No. 196600213D)
140 Paya Lebar Road
#03-11, A-Z Building
Singapore 409015
ATTN: PATRICIA ONG
TEL: 65-6740 9320 FAX: 65-6747 2668

Contents

Demisemiquavers

A demisemiquaver, 𝅘𝅥𝅰 or 𝅘𝅥𝅰 is half the length of a semiquaver.

The demisemiquaver rest is written as 𝄿

Thus:

𝅘𝅥𝅯 lasts as long as 2 𝅘𝅥𝅰s (𝅘𝅥𝅰𝅘𝅥𝅰)

𝅘𝅥𝅮 lasts as long as 4 𝅘𝅥𝅰s (𝅘𝅥𝅰𝅘𝅥𝅰𝅘𝅥𝅰𝅘𝅥𝅰)

Demisemiquavers can be grouped as 𝅘𝅥𝅰𝅘𝅥𝅰𝅘𝅥𝅰𝅘𝅥𝅰𝅘𝅥𝅰𝅘𝅥𝅰𝅘𝅥𝅰𝅘𝅥𝅰 or 𝅘𝅥𝅰𝅘𝅥𝅰𝅘𝅥𝅰𝅘𝅥𝅰 𝅘𝅥𝅰𝅘𝅥𝅰𝅘𝅥𝅰𝅘𝅥𝅰

♩ lasts as long as 8 𝅘𝅥𝅰s (𝅘𝅥𝅰𝅘𝅥𝅰𝅘𝅥𝅰𝅘𝅥𝅰𝅘𝅥𝅰𝅘𝅥𝅰𝅘𝅥𝅰𝅘𝅥𝅰)

𝅘𝅥𝅰𝅘𝅥𝅰𝅘𝅥𝅰 (3) lasts as long as a 𝅘𝅥𝅯

1. Write one note which lasts as long as the number of demisemiquavers in each of the following:
(An example is shown below.)

a) 4 𝅘𝅥𝅰s last as long as a quaver or (𝅘𝅥𝅮)

b) 16 𝅘𝅥𝅰s last as long as a 4 quavers

c) 2 𝅘𝅥𝅰s last as long as a 1 semiquaver 𝅘𝅥𝅯

d) 8 𝅘𝅥𝅰s last as long as a 2 quavers ♩

e) 12 𝅘𝅥𝅰s last as long as a 3 quavers ♩.

f) 32 𝅘𝅥𝅰s last as long as a 8 quavers 𝅝

4. 2. ½

2. Write the correct number in the blank spaces:

a) 𝅗𝅥. lasts as long as 24 𝅘𝅥𝅰s

b) ♪. lasts as long as 6 𝅘𝅥𝅰s

c) ♪ lasts as long as 4 𝅘𝅥𝅰s

d) ♩ lasts as long as 8 𝅘𝅥𝅰s

e) ♩. lasts as long as 12 𝅘𝅥𝅰s

3. Write the correct time signature for each of the following:

a)

b)

c)

d)

e)

f)

g)

h)

4. Add the missing rest or rests at each of the places marked * :

a)

b)

c)

d)

e)

f)

g)

h)

5. Add the missing bar-lines in each of the following which begins on the first beat of the bar:

Notes Beyond Two Ledger Lines

1. Draw notes between the two given notes using ledger lines, then name them:

2. Give the letter name of these notes and then write them at the same pitch in the other clef:

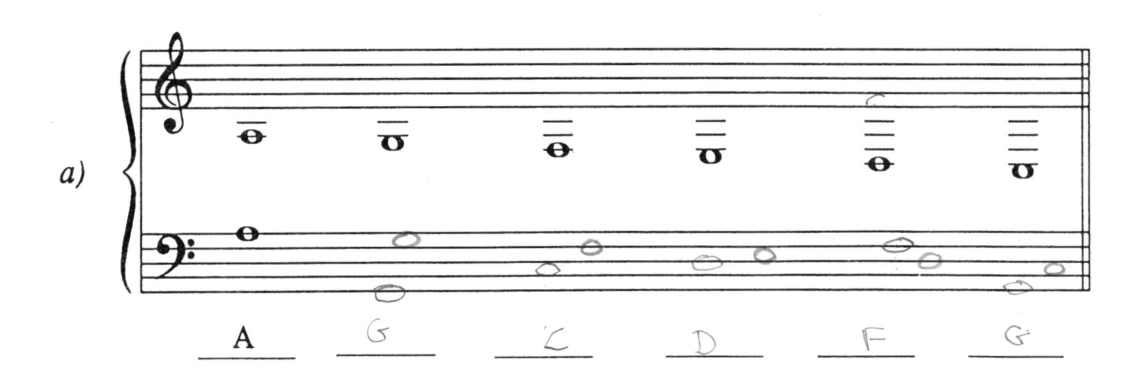

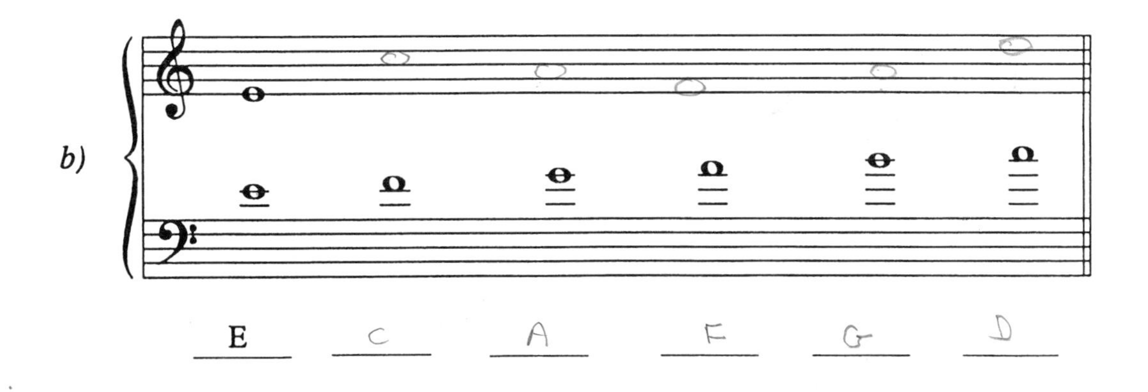

3. Write these notes using ledger lines ***above the stave*** only:

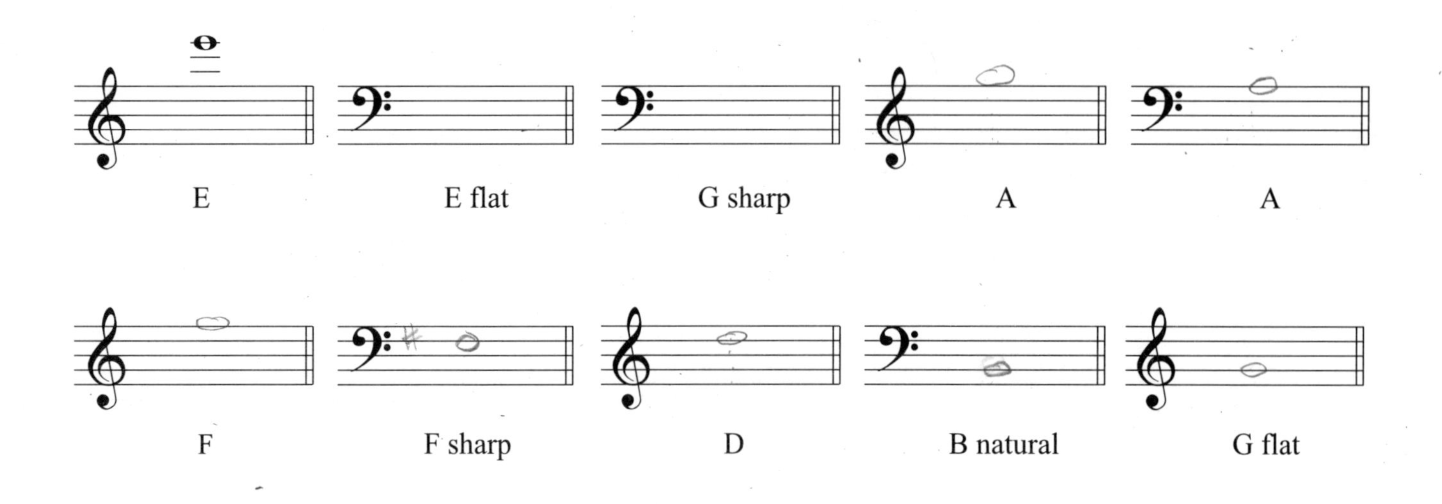

4. Write these notes using ledger lines ***below the stave*** only:

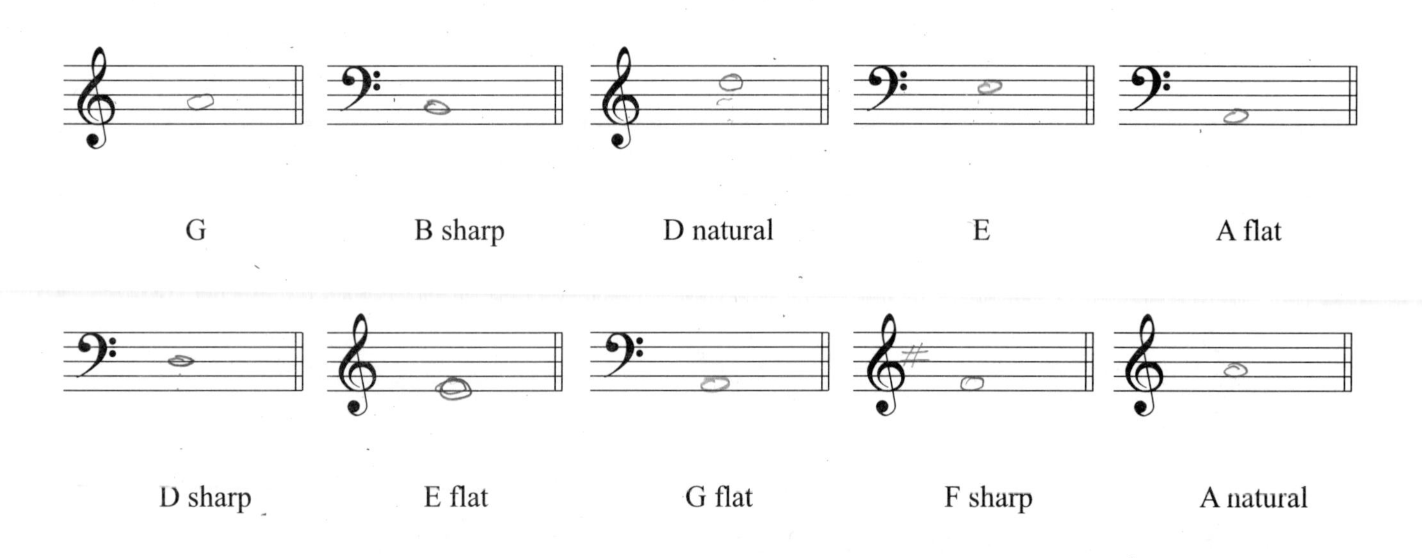

5. Rewrite each of the following in the other clef, but at the same pitch:

e.g.

Bloch, Quartet
a)
3
3
etc.
© G. Schirmer Inc. All rights reserved. International copyright secured.
Reproduced with permission of G. Schimer (Australia) Pty Ltd.
Chopin, Sonata in G minor
b)
Debussy, Petite Suite
c)
Shostakovich, Symphony No.7 Op.60
d)
J.S. Bach, Fugue No.24 (from the '48', Bk.2)
e)
etc.

Transposition

Transposition takes place when a group of notes is moved up or down, and the intervals between the notes remain unchanged.

The notes have been transposed ***up an octave.***

Likewise, notes in the treble clef can also be transposed ***down an octave*** to the bass clef.

You may use a keyboard or your instrument to make sure that your transposition is ***by an octave*** in the exercises that follow.

1. Transpose these notes ***down an octave*** using the bass clef:

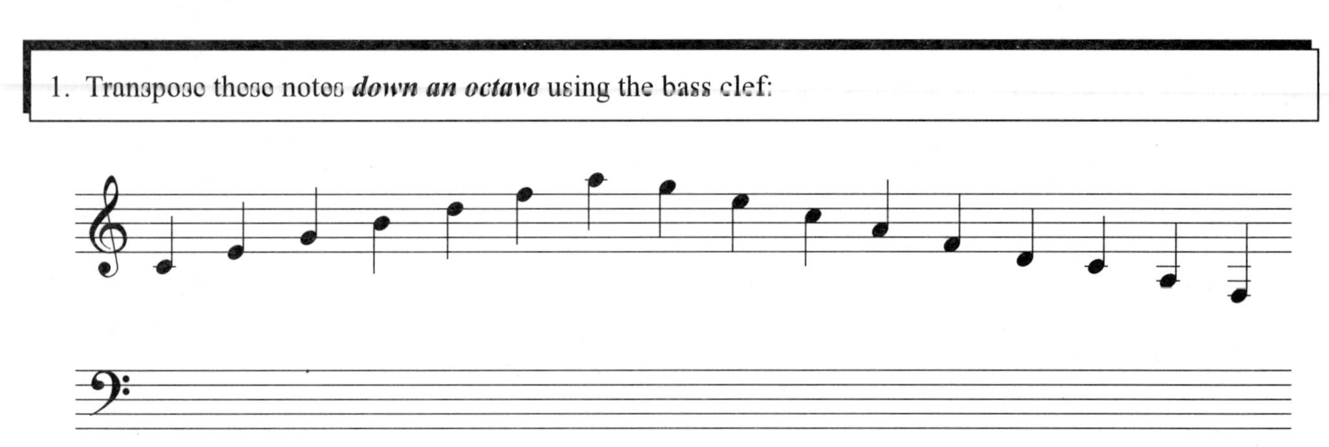

2. Transpose these notes ***up an octave*** using the treble clef:

3. Transpose the following ***down an octave***, using the bass clef:

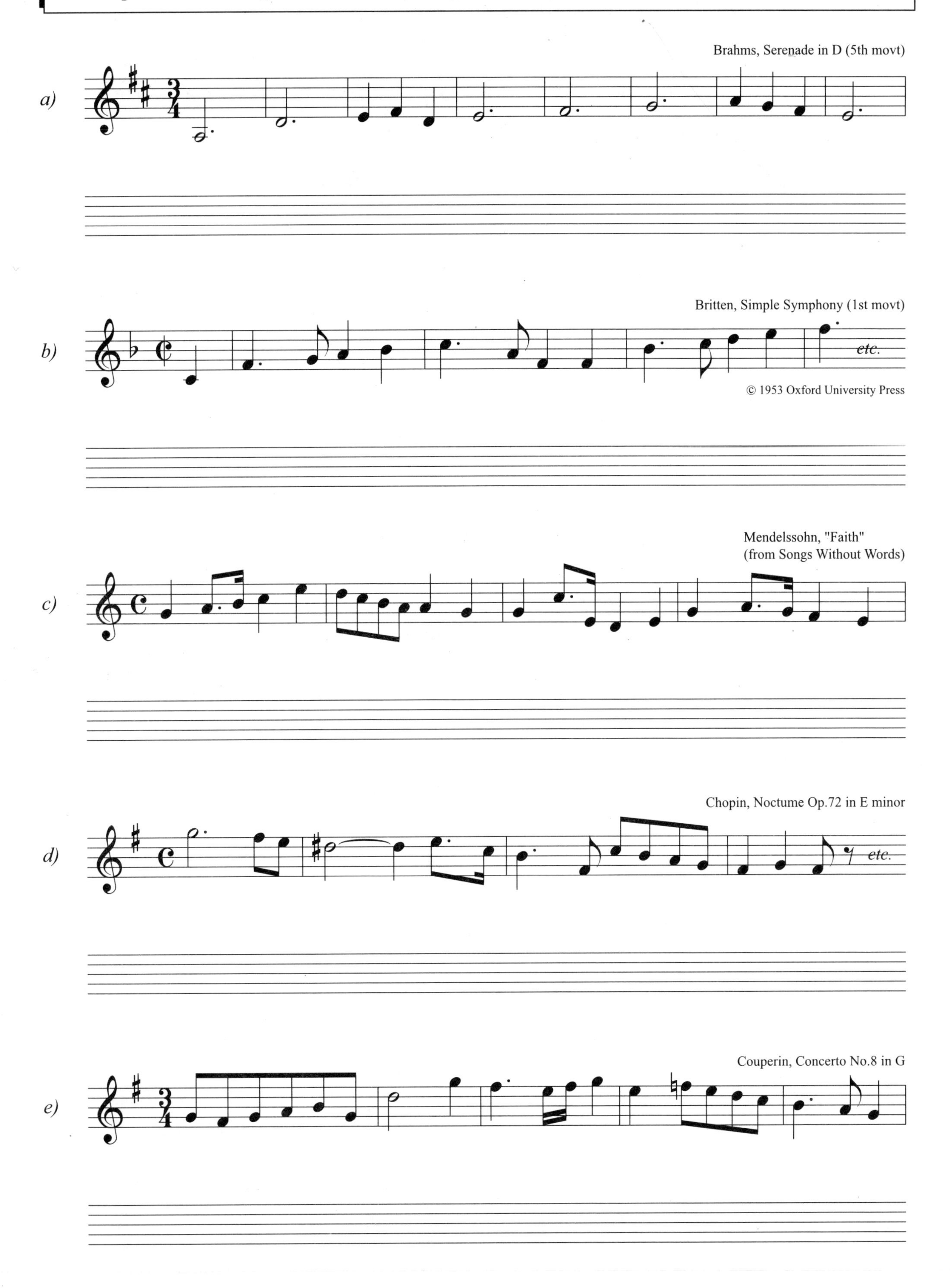

4. Transpose the following ***up an octave***, using the treble clef :

Granados, Spanish Dance No.6

a)

etc.

Beethoven, Leonore No.2

b)

Prokofiev, String Quartet No.1 in B minor
Op.50 (2nd movt.)

c)

Byrd, Pavan

d)

J.S. Bach, Toccata & Fugue in C minor

e)

The Keys of E Major and A♭ Major

The scales of E major and A♭ major follow the pattern of tones and semitones in all major scales:

E major, ascending (with slurred semitones)

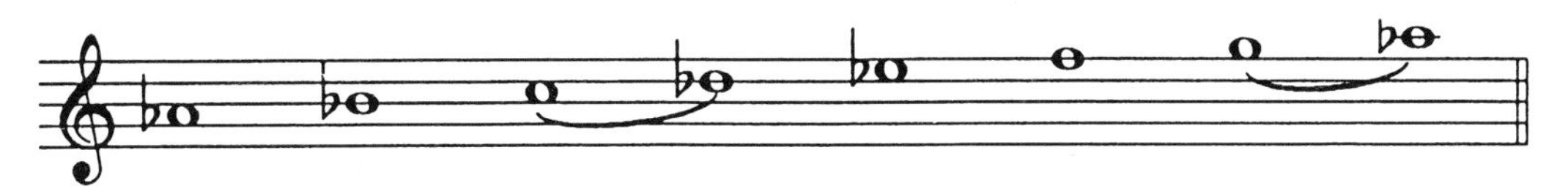

A♭ major, ascending (with slurred semitones)

The key signatures can thus be written as:

The tonic triads are:

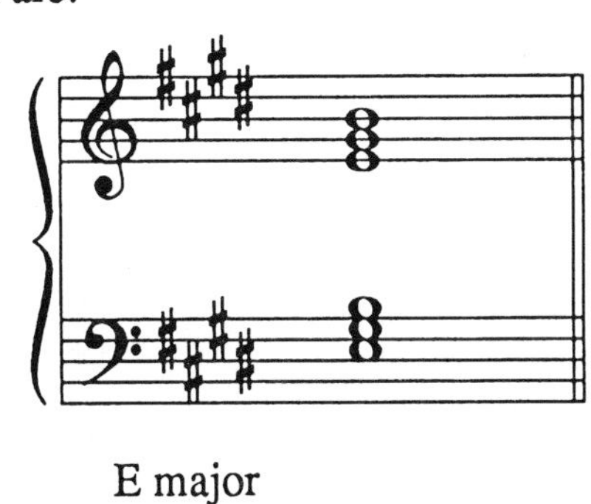

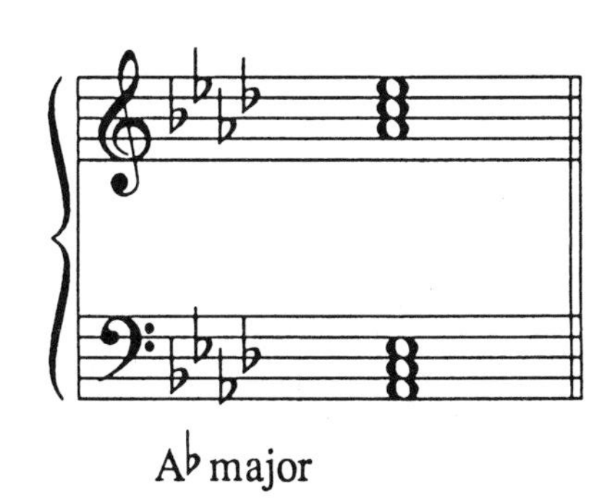

1. Without using key signatures, write the following scales. Use the given rhythms and slur the semitones:

2. Using the correct key signatures, write the following scales. Use the given rhythms:

3. Write the tonic triad of each of the following. Do not use the key signature:

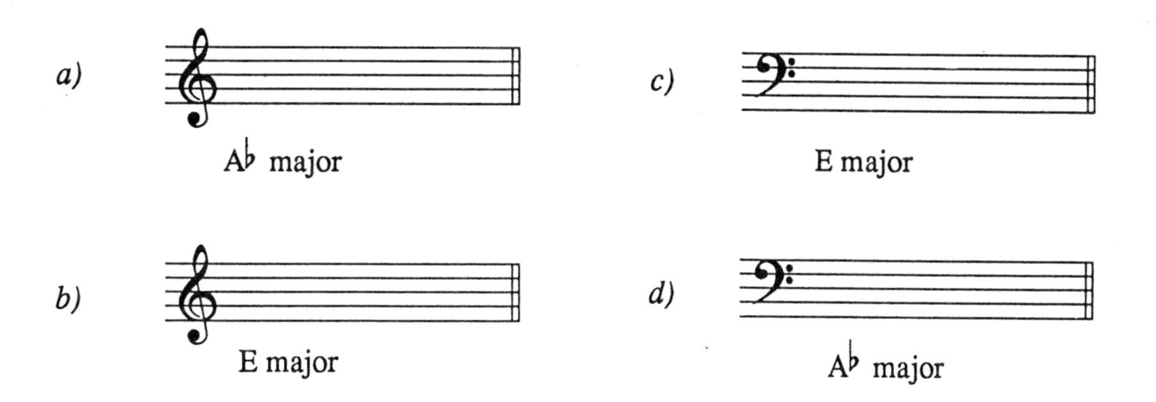

4. Insert the necessary accidentals into the melodies. The key has been named in each case:
(This exercise includes all other major keys that have been covered in the previous two grades.)

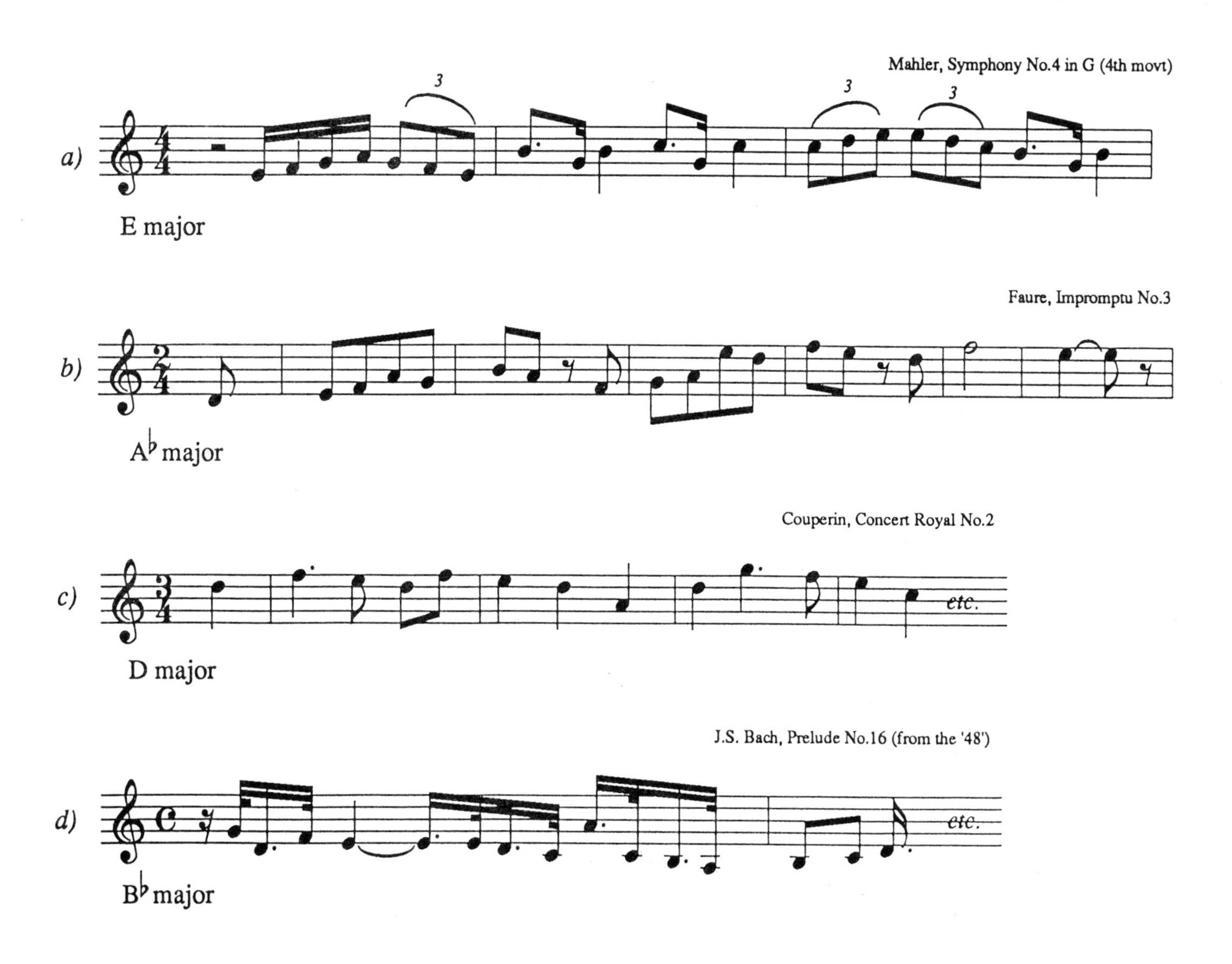

Beethoven, Quartet in F

Schubert, Waltz Op.50

Verdi, March from Aida

Copland, Rodeo (Saturday Night Waltz)

Tchaikovsky, Symphony No.2

Brahms, Tragic Overture

Compound Time

In ***simple time***, a beat is divided into two equal parts:

and

Sometimes a beat may be divided into a triplet:

and

In ***compound time***, a beat can be divided **regularly** into three parts:

There are three types of compound time:

Compound duple (2 dotted crotchet beats in a bar)

Compound triple (3 dotted crotchet beats in a bar)

iii)

Compound quadruple (4 dotted crotchet beats in a bar)

Notice that the beats used are ***dotted crotchets***.

In ***simple time***, the beats are in crotchets, minims or quavers:

Simple duple

i)

2 crotchet beats in a bar

ii)

2 minim beats in a bar

Simple triple

i)

3 crotchet beats in a bar

ii)

3 quaver beats in a bar

iii)

3 minim beats in a bar

Simple quadruple

i)

4 crotchet beats in a bar

ii)

4 minim beats in a bar

1. Describe the kind of time in each of the following and write a bar of quavers. An example is given:

e.g. $\frac{3}{2}$

Kind of time : Simple triple (3 minim beats in a bar)

a) $\frac{6}{8}$

Kind of time : ____________________( )

b) $\frac{12}{8}$

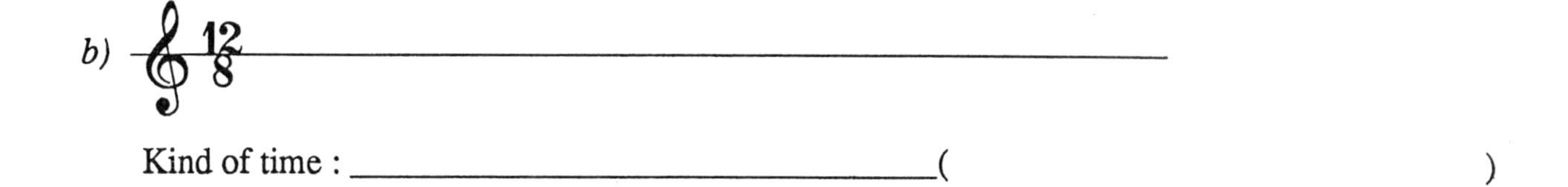

Kind of time : ____________________( )

c) $\frac{4}{4}$

Kind of time : ____________________( )

d) $\frac{2}{2}$

Kind of time : ____________________( )

e) $\frac{3}{4}$

Kind of time : ____________________( )

f) $\frac{9}{8}$

Kind of time : ____________________( )

g) $\frac{2}{4}$

Kind of time : ______________________________ (   )

h) $\frac{3}{8}$

Kind of time : ______________________________ (   )

i) $\frac{4}{2}$

Kind of time : ______________________________ (   )

2. Add the time signature at the beginning of each of the following and then complete the sentences below. (Follow the example.):

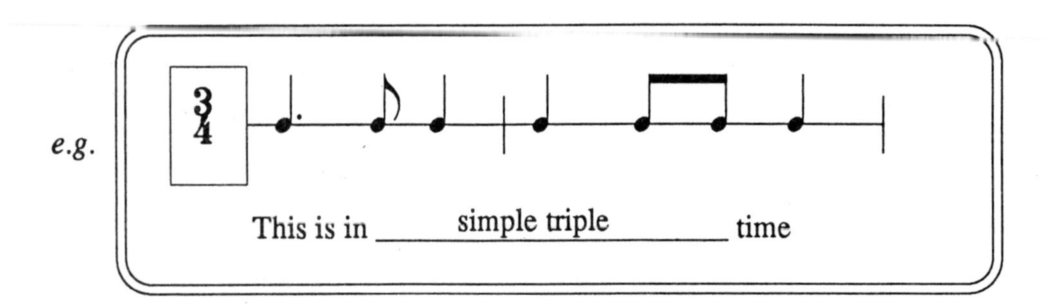

a)

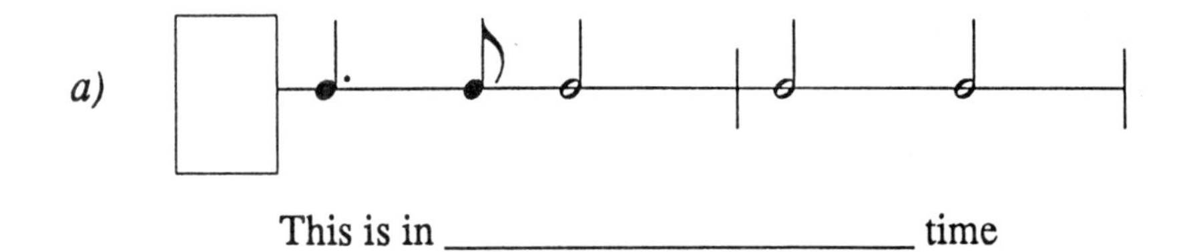

This is in ____________________ time

b)

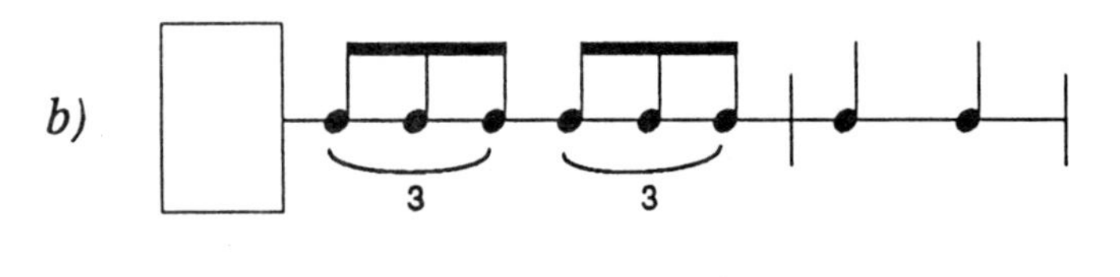

This is in ____________________ time

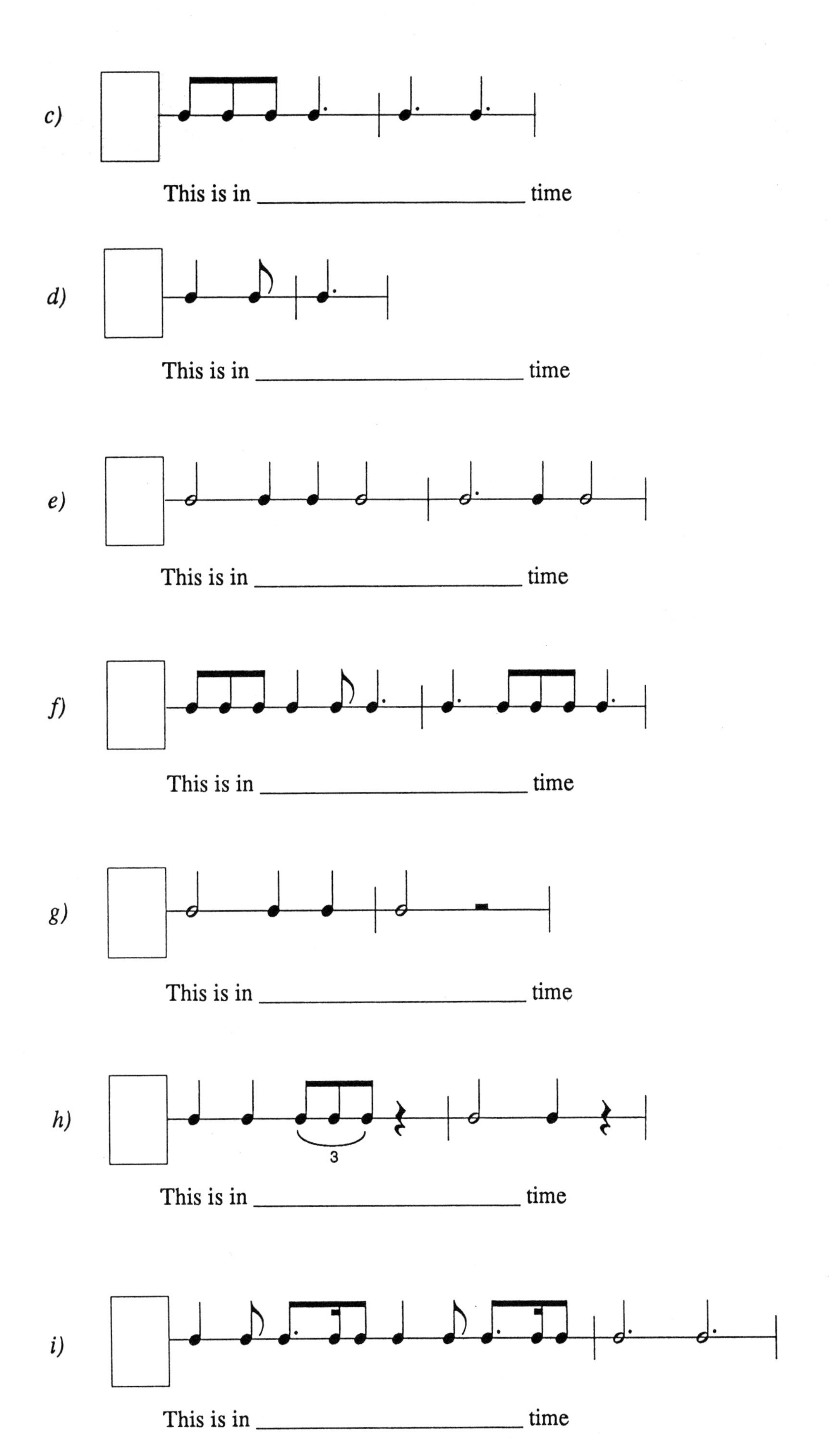
c)
This is in ______________________ time
d)
This is in ______________________ time
e)
This is in ______________________ time
f)
This is in ______________________ time
g)
This is in ______________________ time
h)
3
This is in ______________________ time
i)
This is in ______________________ time

3. Add the correct time signature in each of the following and then describe the kind of time:

Beethoven, Sonata in G Op.31 No.1
h)
Kind of time:
Franck, Symphonic Variations
i)
Kind of time:
Ibert, Escales
j)
Kind of time:
© Reproduced by permission of Editions A. Leduc Paris
United Music Publishers Ltd
Frescobaldi, Capriccio La Spagnoletta
k)
Kind of time:
Roussel, Le Festin de L'Araignee
l)
Kind of time:
Britten, Phantasy Quartet
m)
Kind of time:
© Copyright 1935 by Hawkes & Son (London) Ltd
Prokofiev, Sonata No.3 (5th movt)
n)
Kind of time:

4. Add the missing bar-lines in each of the following which begins on the first beat of the bar:

A melody or a piece of music can be written in simple or compound time (and vice versa) without changing the musical effect:

5. Rewrite the following melodies using the new time signatures: (Do not change the musical effect.)

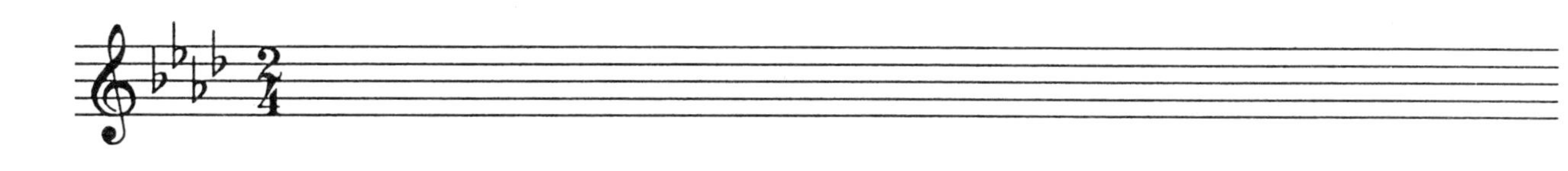

c)

d)
Liszt, Concerto No.1
etc.
e)
Vaughan Williams, March of the Kitchen Utensils
© Novello & Company Limited. Used by permission.
f)
Tchaikovsky, The Sleeping Beauty
g)
Mendelssohn, Quartet No.3
h)
Britten, Simple Symphony (2nd movt)
© 1935 Oxford University Press

Groupings in Compound Time

Grouping of Notes

i) A note for a full bar in ***compound time*** is written as:

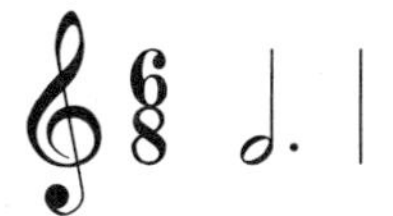

ii) Notes for each beat are written as:

iii) Notes for each beat can also be divided into ♩ ♪ or ♪ ♩ or ♩. :

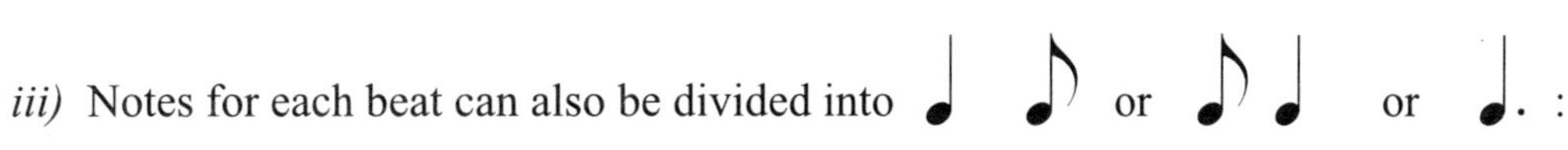

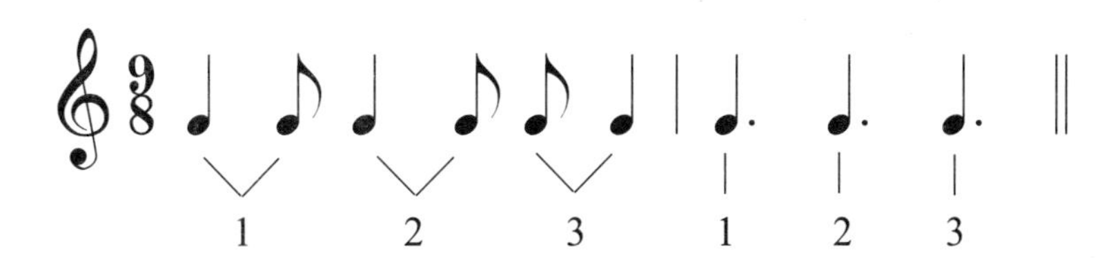

iv) Shorter notes are beamed into **threes** to show the division of beats:

1. Rewrite each of the following rhythms with the notes correctly grouped: (You may circle the notes to form the beat or beats before you begin.)

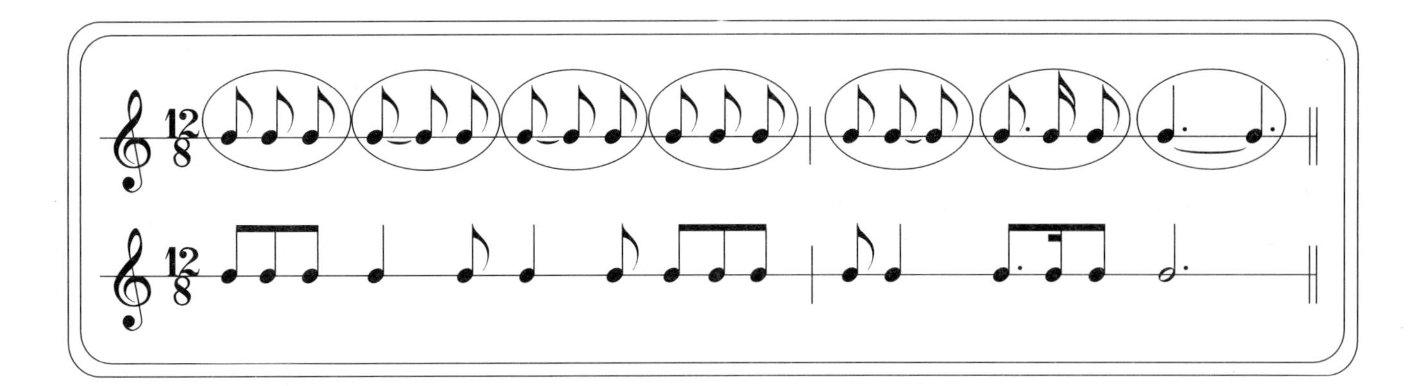

2. Rewrite each of the following melodies with the notes correctly grouped.

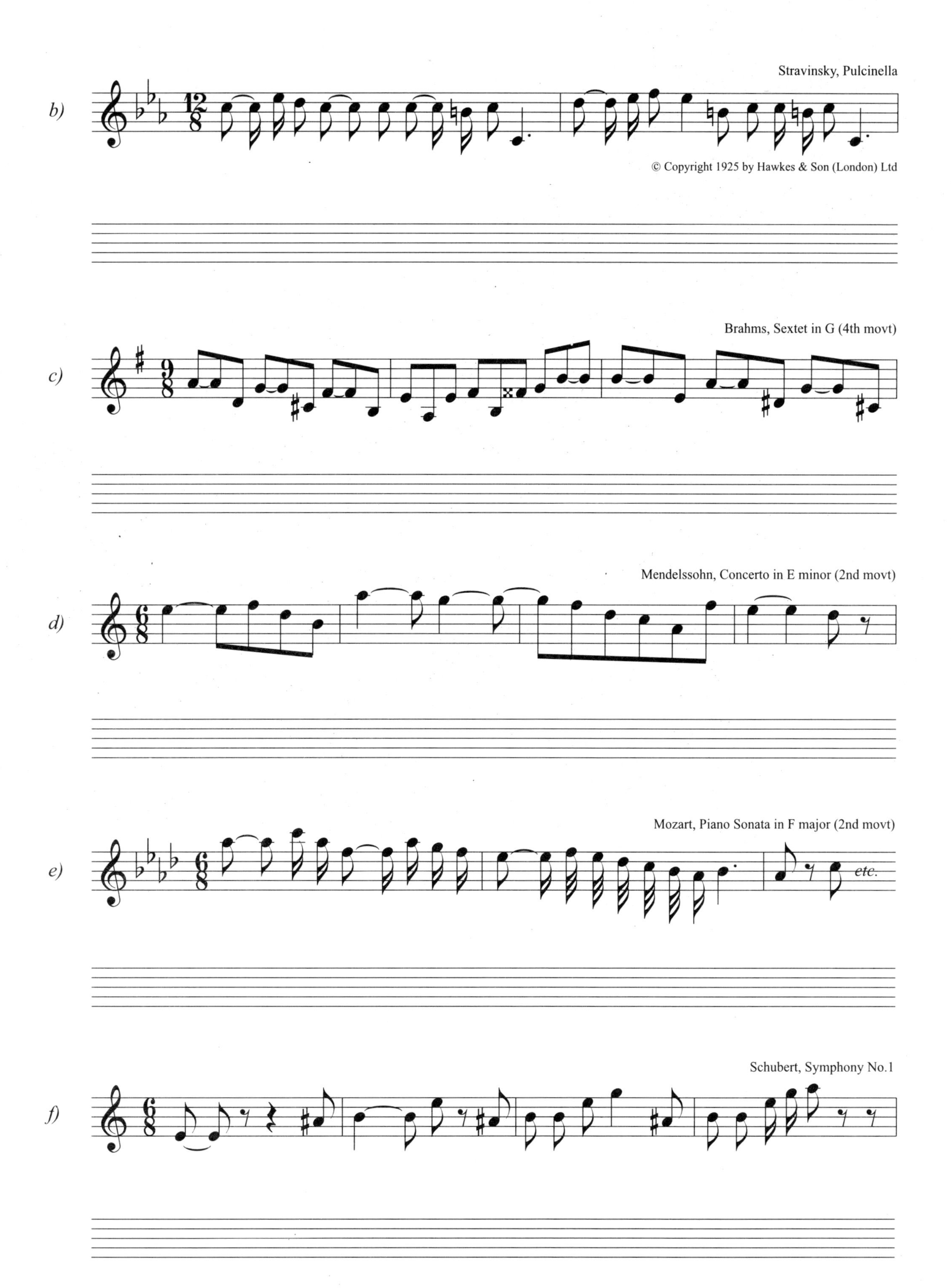
Stravinsky, Pulcinella
b)
© Copyright 1925 by Hawkes & Son (London) Ltd
Brahms, Sextet in G (4th movt)
c)
Mendelssohn, Concerto in E minor (2nd movt)
d)
Mozart, Piano Sonata in F major (2nd movt)
e)
etc.
Schubert, Symphony No.1
f)

Grouping of Rests

In Compound time:

i) The rest for a full bar is written as ▬ . It is called a **bar** rest.

ii) The rest or rests for a beat can be written as 𝄽· or 𝄽 𝄾 :

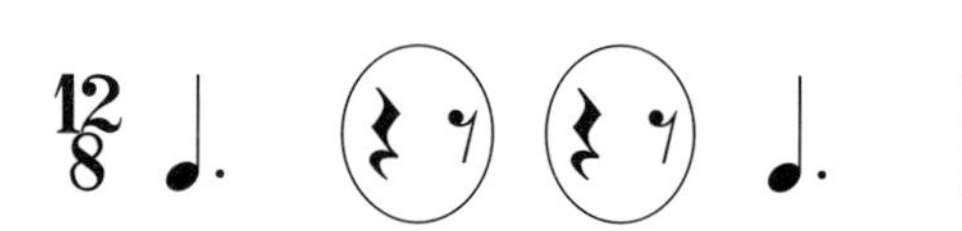

In 12/8 silence for the first half or second half of the bar may be written as ▬· :

iii) The three units of each beat must be grouped as:

(𝄽 ♪) or

2 + 1

1 + 1 + 1

Never:

(♪ 𝄽)

1 + 2

Thus:

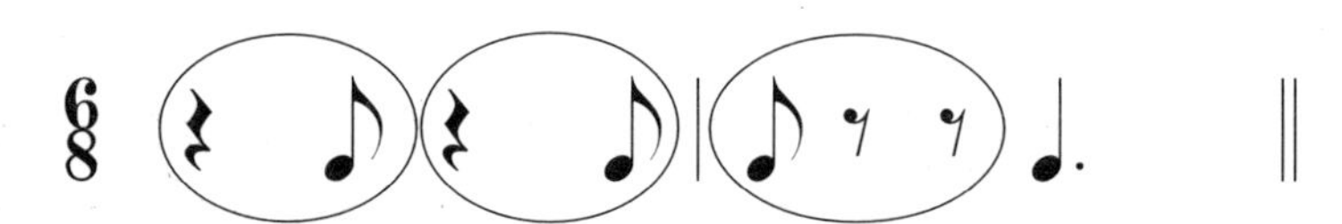

i*v)* When shorter values of rests are used, each quaver beat must have a new rest:

1. Add *one rest* at each of the places marked * :

a) * *

b) * *

c) * *

d) * *

e) * * *

f) * * *

g) * *

h) * * *

2. Complete each of these bars with a rest or rests at the places marked * :

a)

b)

c)

d)

e)

f)

g)

h)

i)

j)

k)

l)

m)

n)

o)

p)

q)

r)

3. Add one rest or rests at the places marked * so as to complete the bars:

b) 6/8

c) 2/4

d) 9/8

e) 4/4

f) 3/8

g) 12/8

h) 4/2

The Minor Scales: Melodic and Harmonic

In grade 3, the student must know both the harmonic and the melodic forms of the minor scales.

The table below shows the keys that have to be known:

Minor key	Key Signature	Harmonic form raise 7th note in ascending & decending scales	Melodic form ascending: raise 6th & 7th notes	 descending: lower 7th & 6th notes
A	_____	G♯	F♯ G♯	G♮ F♮
E	F♯	D♯	C♯ D♯	D♮ C♮
B	F♯ C♯	A♯	G♯ A♯	A♮ G♮
F♯	F♯ C♯ G♯	E♯	D♯ E♯	E♮ D♮
C♯	F♯ C♯ G♯ D♯	B♯	A♯ B♯	B♮ A♮
D	B♭	C♯	B♮ C♯	C♮ B♭
G	B♭ E♭	F♯	E♮ F♯	F♮ E♭
C	B♭ E♭ A♭	B♮	A♮ B♮	B♭ A♭
F	B♭ E♭ A♭ D♭	E♮	D♮ E♮	E♭ D♭

For example, the B minor scale can be written as:

i) **B harmonic minor**

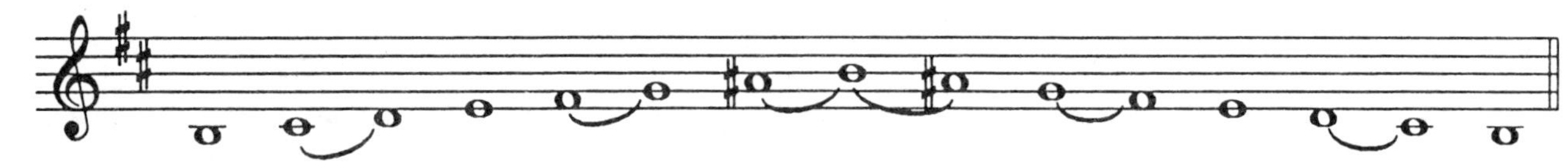

ii) **B melodic minor**

The tonic triad may be written as:

B minor, with
key signature

B minor, without
key signature

1. Write the necessary accidentals to make the scales named. Do not use any key signature. Mark each pair of semitones with a slur:

a)

G harmonic minor

b)

D melodic minor

c)

F♯ harmonic minor

d)

B melodic minor

e)

C♯ harmonic minor

f)

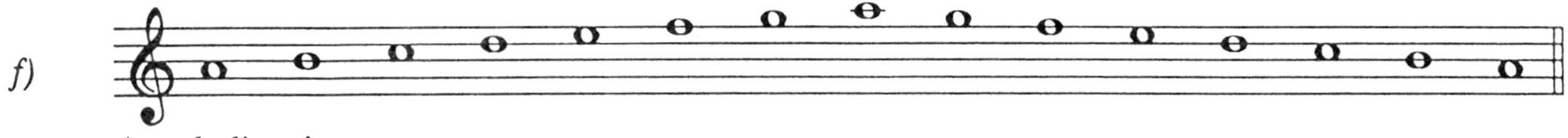

A melodic minor

g)

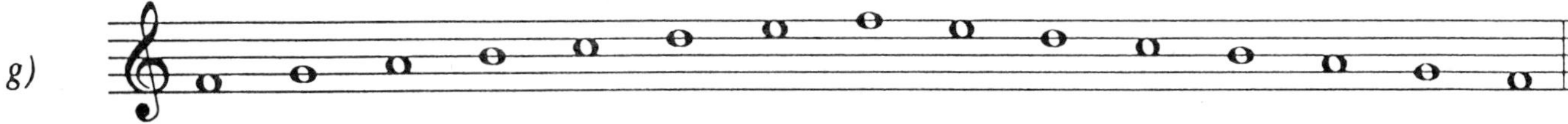

F melodic minor

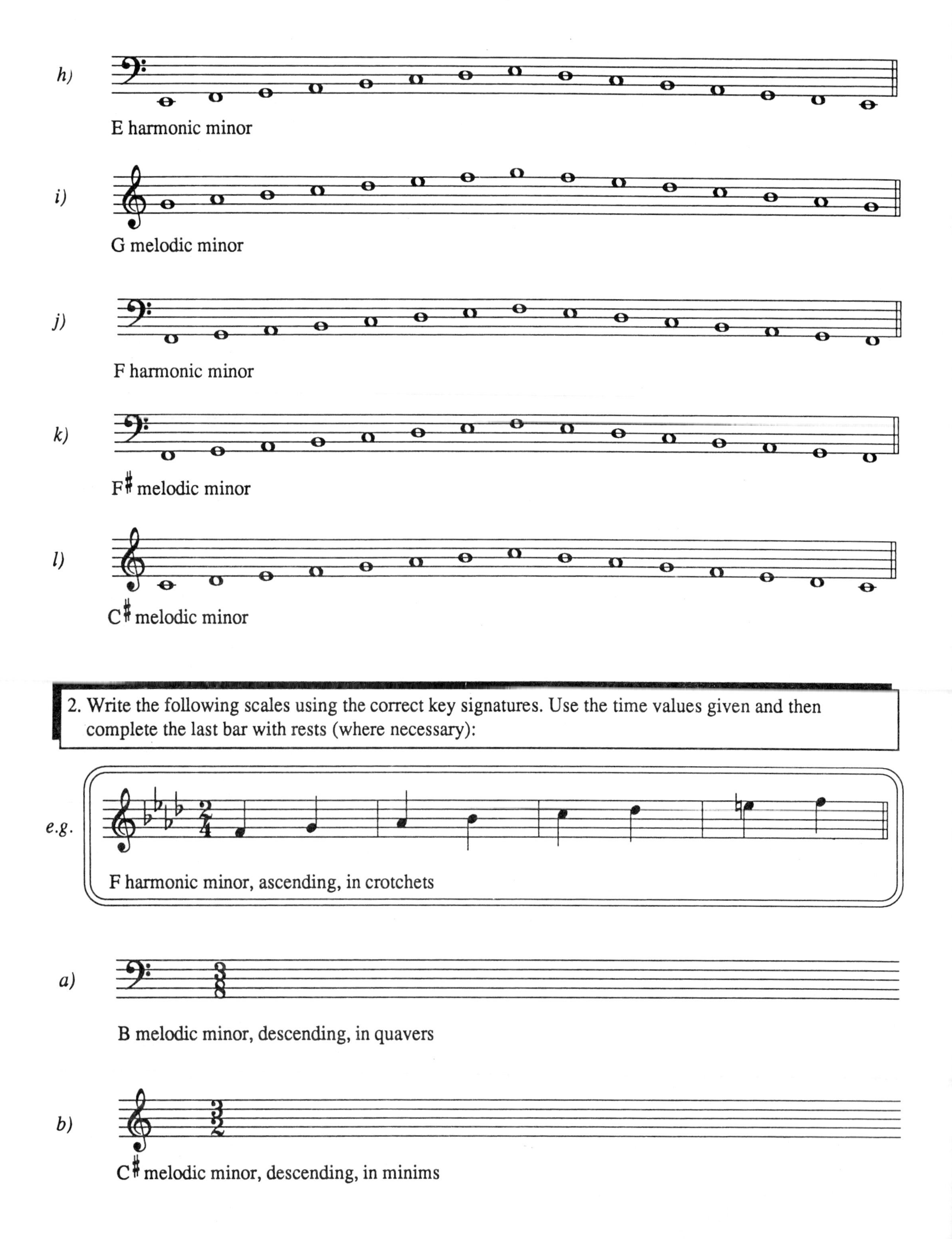
h)
E harmonic minor
i)
G melodic minor
j)
F harmonic minor
k)
F♯ melodic minor
l)
C♯ melodic minor
2. Write the following scales using the correct key signatures. Use the time values given and then complete the last bar with rests (where necessary):
e.g.
F harmonic minor, ascending, in crotchets
a)
B melodic minor, descending, in quavers
b)
C♯ melodic minor, descending, in minims

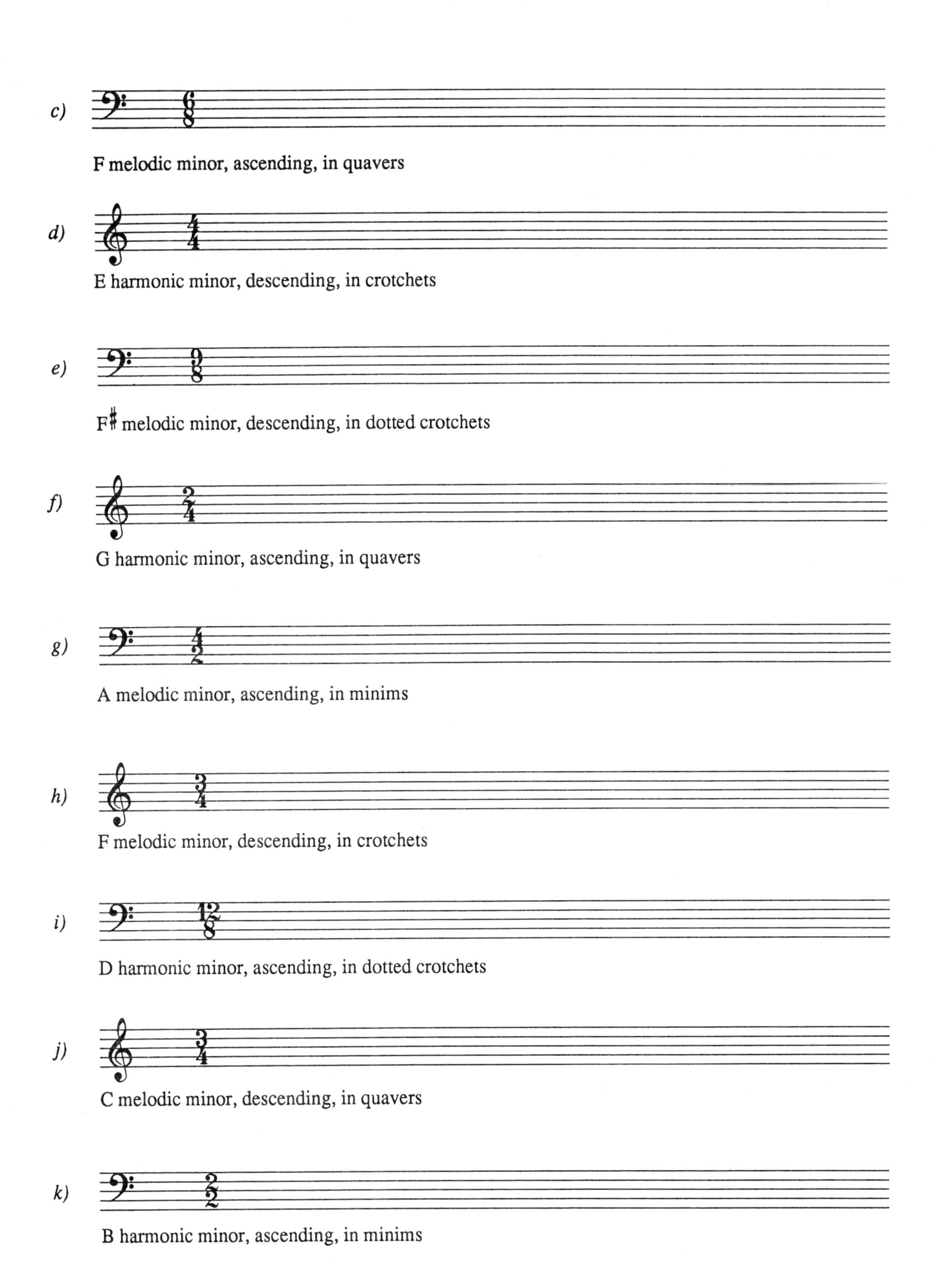

c)
F melodic minor, ascending, in quavers
d)
E harmonic minor, descending, in crotchets
e)
F♯ melodic minor, descending, in dotted crotchets
f)
G harmonic minor, ascending, in quavers
g)
A melodic minor, ascending, in minims
h)
F melodic minor, descending, in crotchets
i)
D harmonic minor, ascending, in dotted crotchets
j)
C melodic minor, descending, in quavers
k)
B harmonic minor, ascending, in minims

3. Write the tonic triad for each of the following keys without using key signatures:

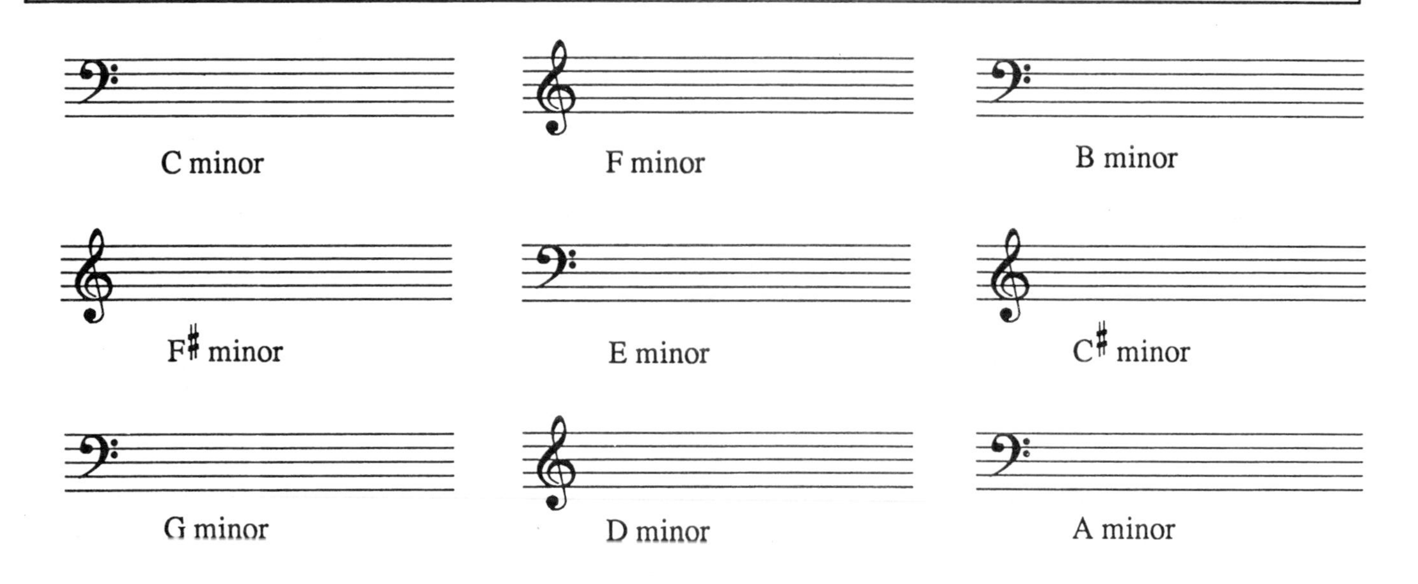

4. Write the correct clef and key signature for each of the following:

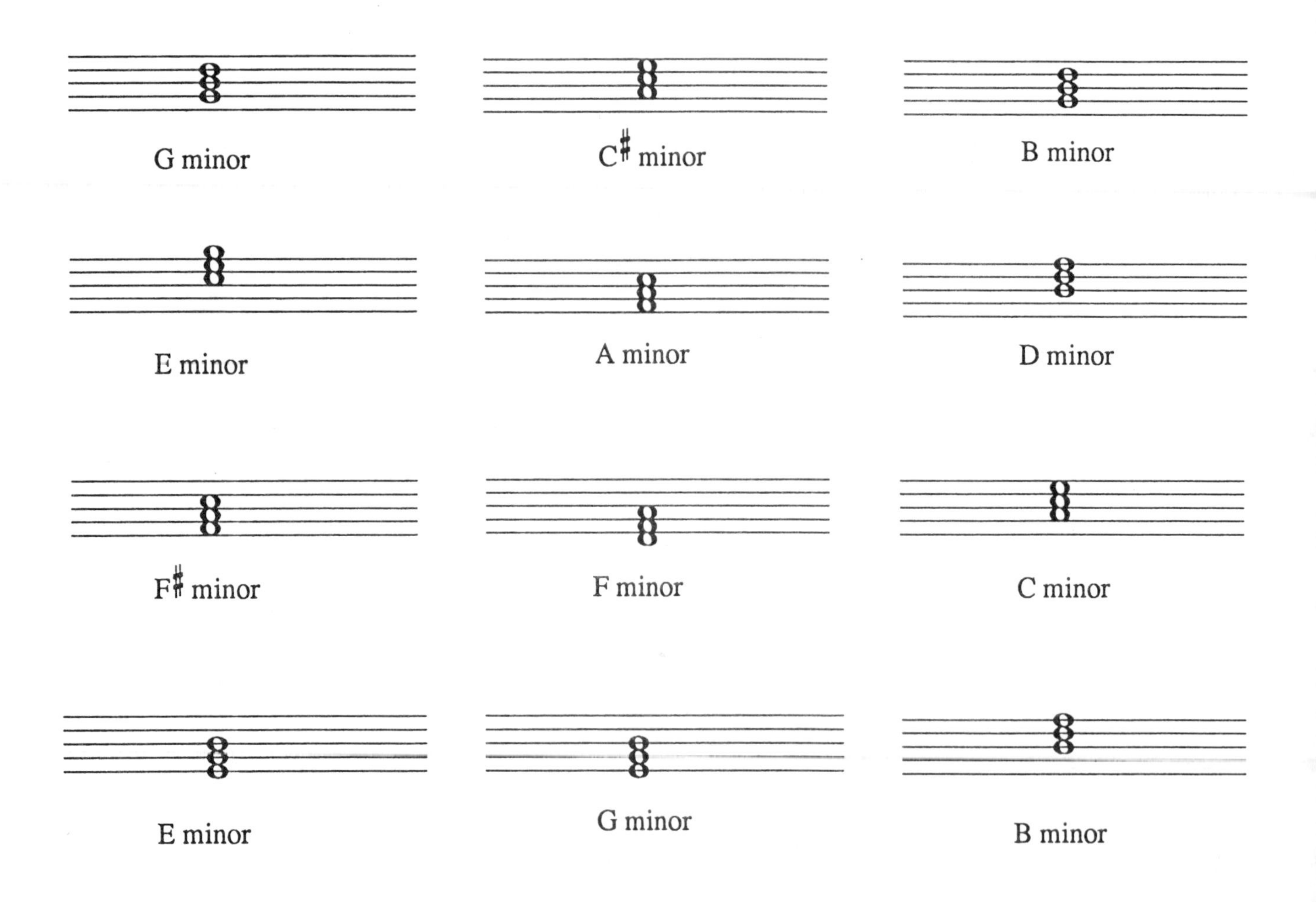

Supplementary Practice in Major and Minor Keys

1. Name the key of each of the following scales. Remember to state whether a minor key is in the melodic or harmonic form:

i)

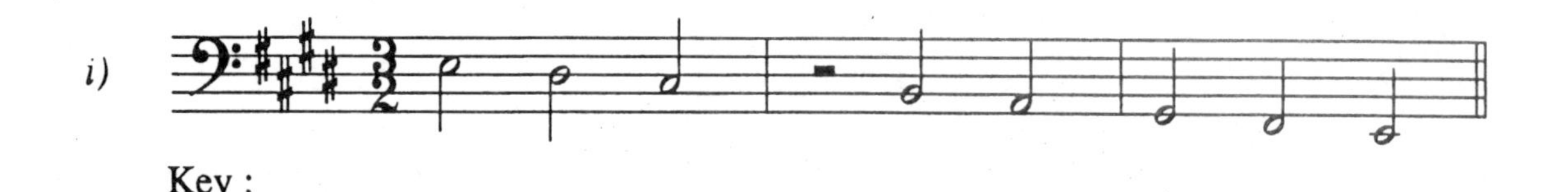

Key : ____________________

j)

Key : ____________________

k)

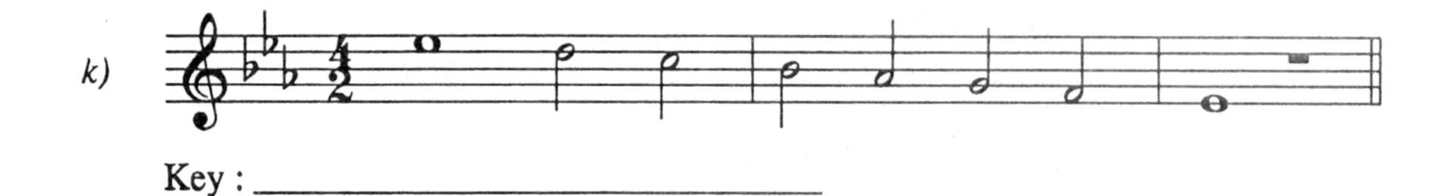

Key : ____________________

l)

Key : ____________________

2. Name four scales which contain the following notes. Melodic and harmonic minors are considered different scales:

a)

1. ____________________
2. ____________________
3. ____________________
4. ____________________

b)

1. ____________________
2. ____________________
3. ____________________
4. ____________________

c)

1. ____________________
2. ____________________
3. ____________________
4. ____________________

3. Name the key of each of the following extracts. Then rewrite them using the correct key signatures. Remember that not all accidentals are to be removed:

J.S. Bach, from the '48'
c)
etc.
Key :
Mahler, "Resurrection" Symphony
d)
Key :
Mendelssohn, Quartet No.4
e)
etc.
Key :
Handel, Concerto No.1
f)
Key :
Corelli, Concerto Grosso in G minor (1st movt)
g)
etc.
Key :

h)
Tchaikovsky, "Pathetic" Symphony
Key :
i)
Mendelssohn, Boat Song
etc.
Key :
j)
Haydn, Trio in G (2nd movt)
Key :
k)
Falla, Suite Populaire
etc.
Key :
l)
Schumann, Sonata in A minor (2nd movt)
etc.
Key :

4. Without using any key signatures, add the correct clef and accidentals to form the scales named:

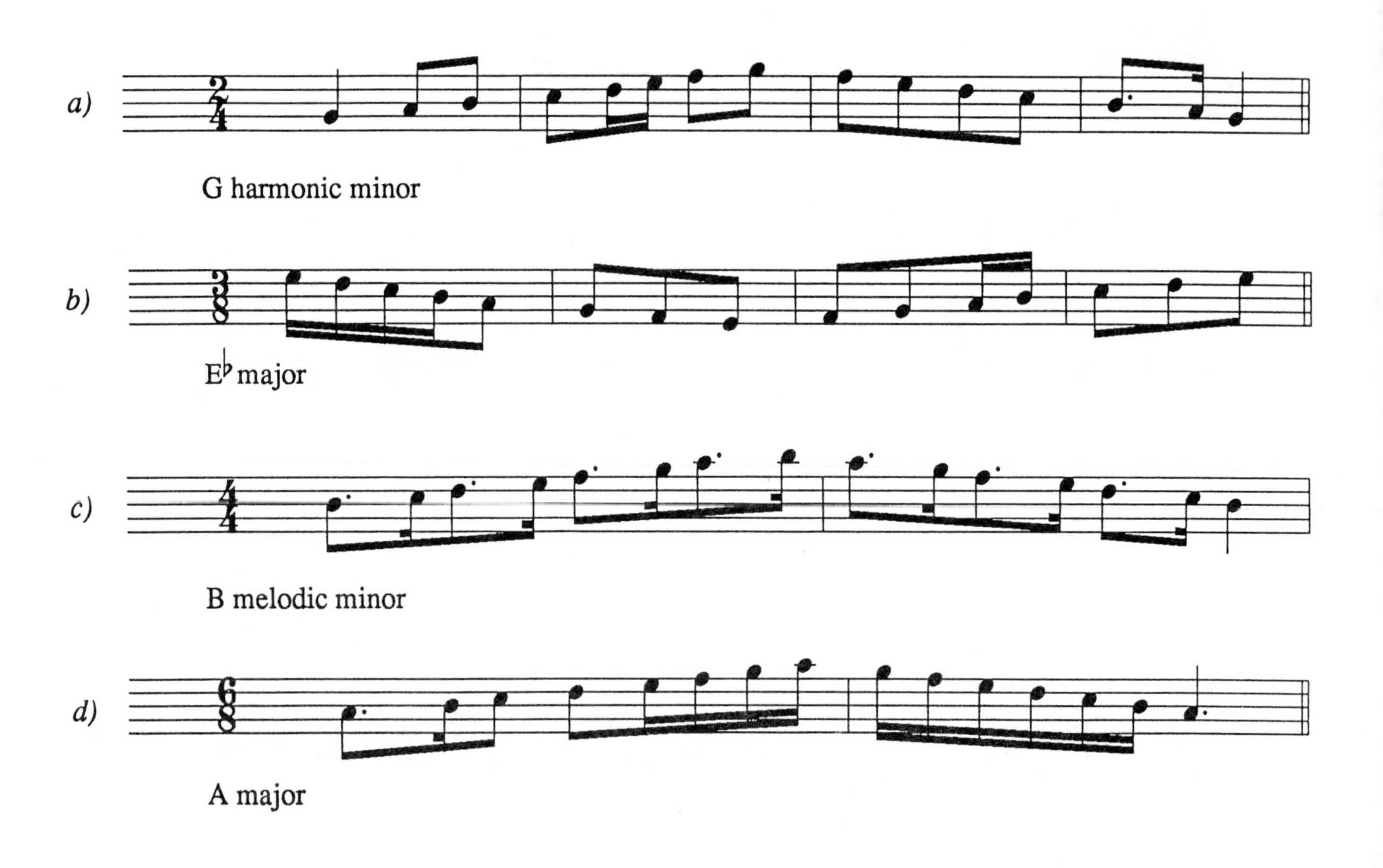

5. Write the tonic triads of each of the following keys without using key signatures:

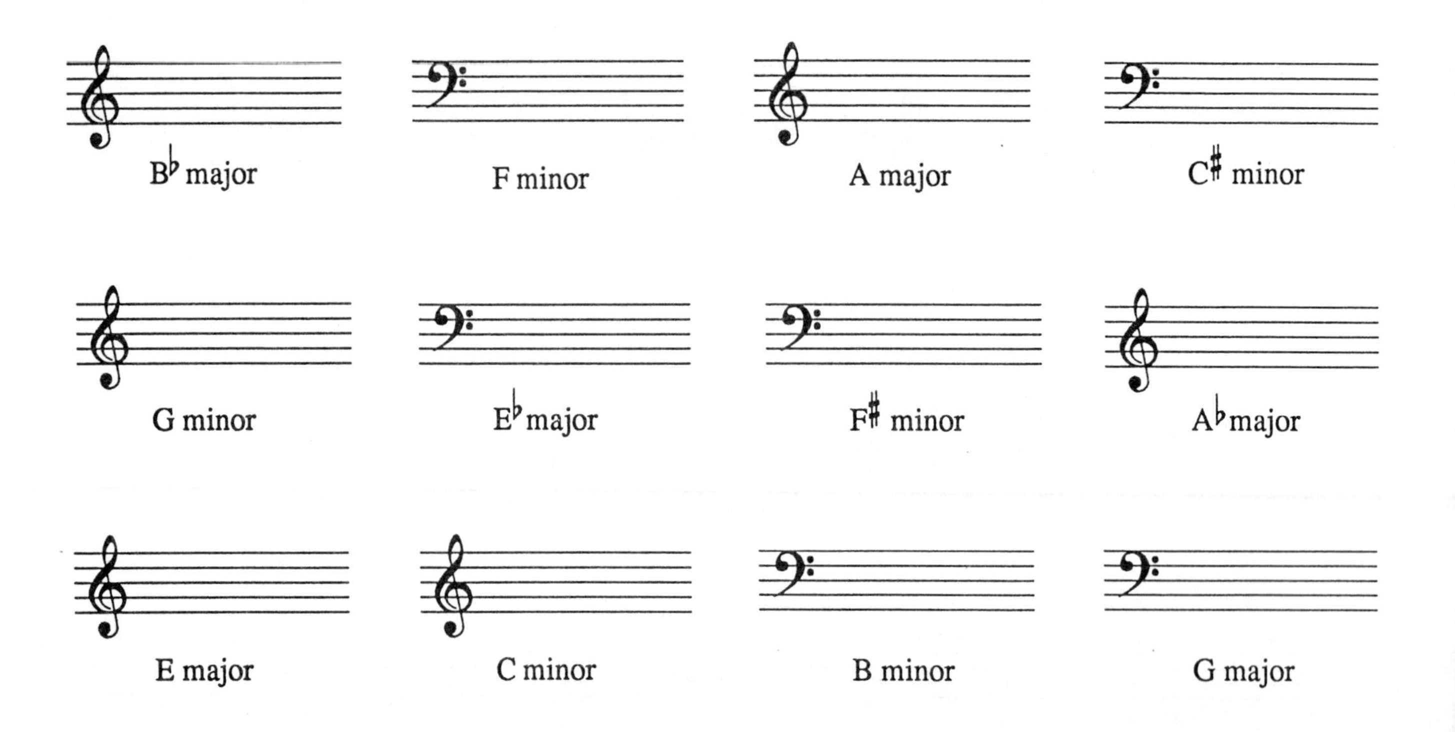

6. Name the keys of these tonic triads:

a) 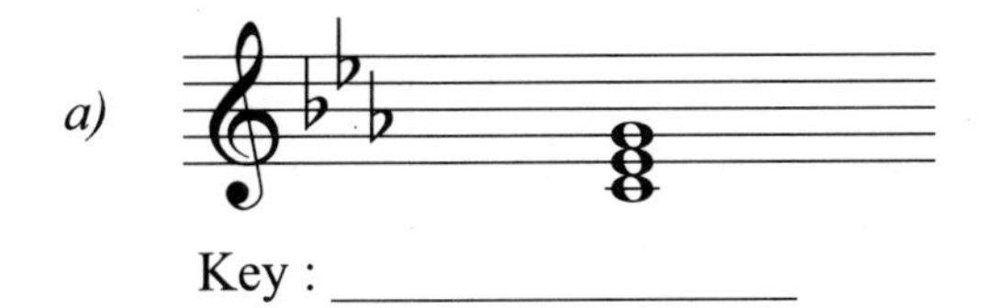

Key : ________________

b) 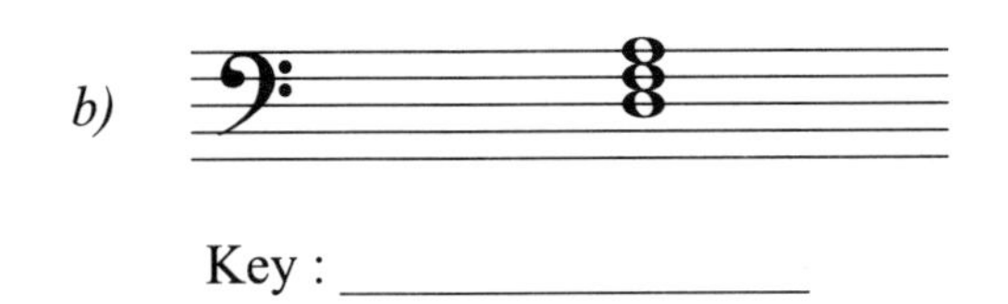

Key : ________________

c) 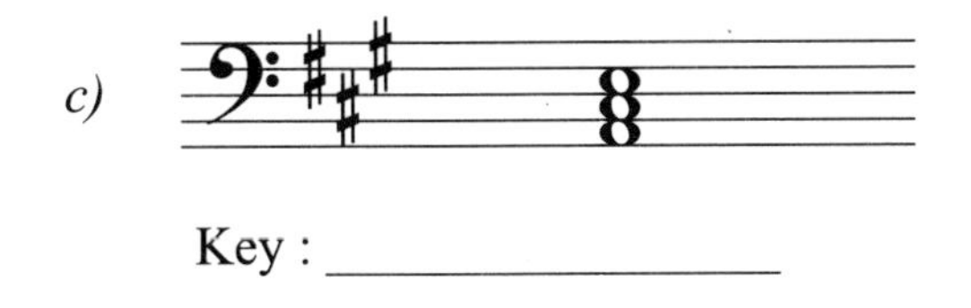

Key : ________________

d) 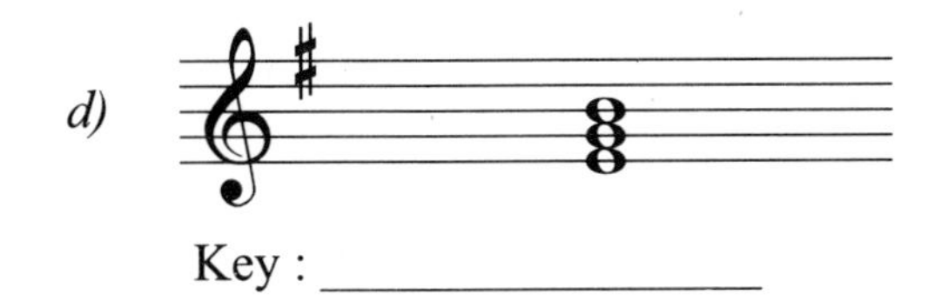

Key : ________________

e) 

Key : ________________

f) 

Key : ________________

g) 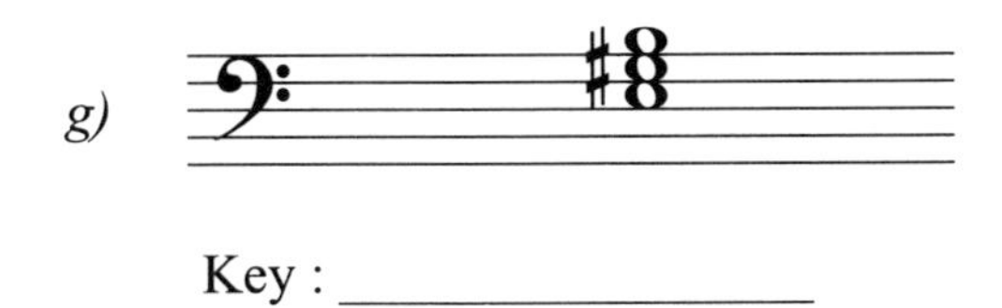

Key : ________________

h) 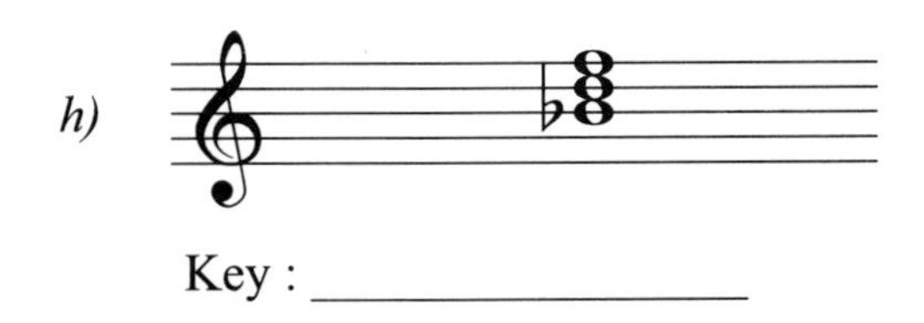

Key : ________________

i) 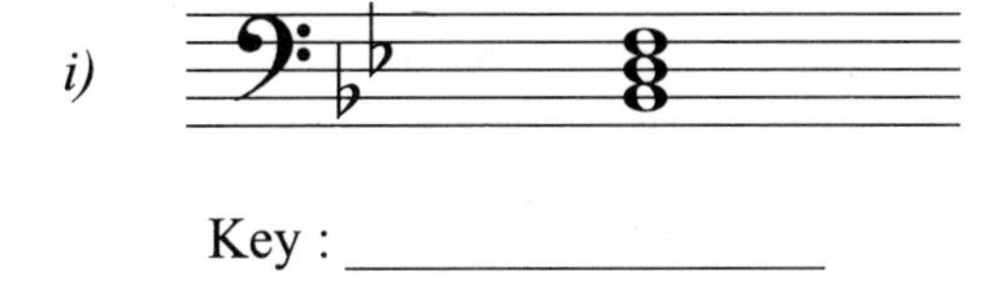

Key : ________________

j) 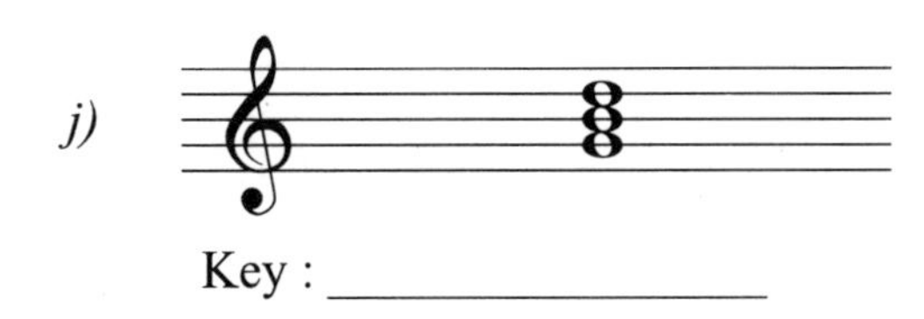

Key : ________________

k) 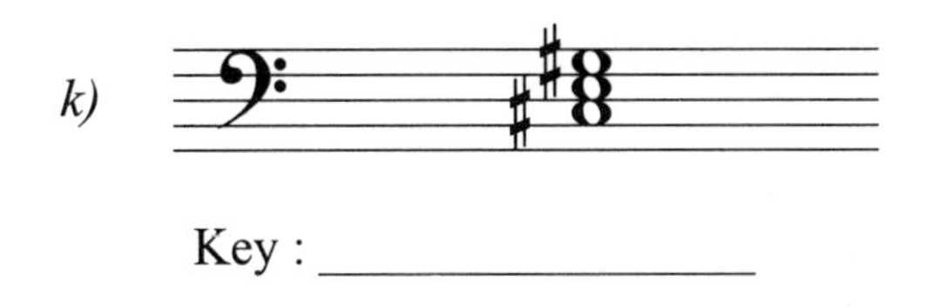

Key : ________________

l) 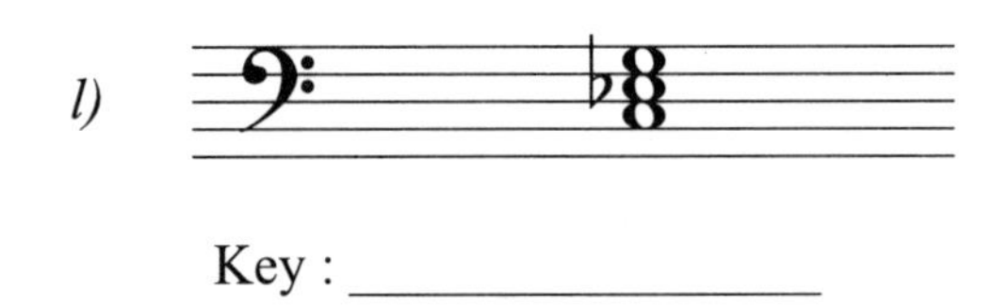

Key : ________________

m) 

Key : ________________

n) 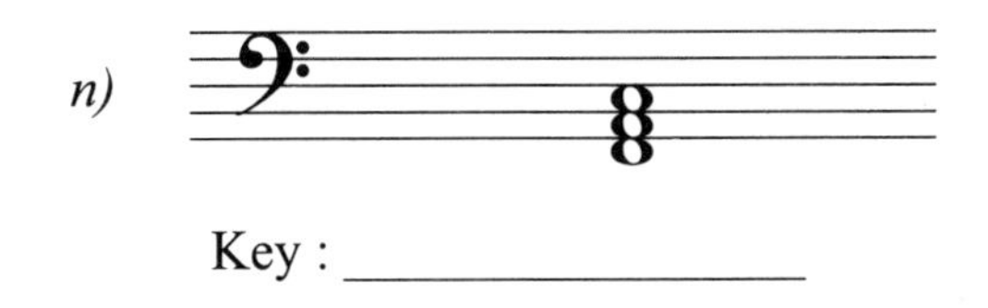

Key : ________________

o) 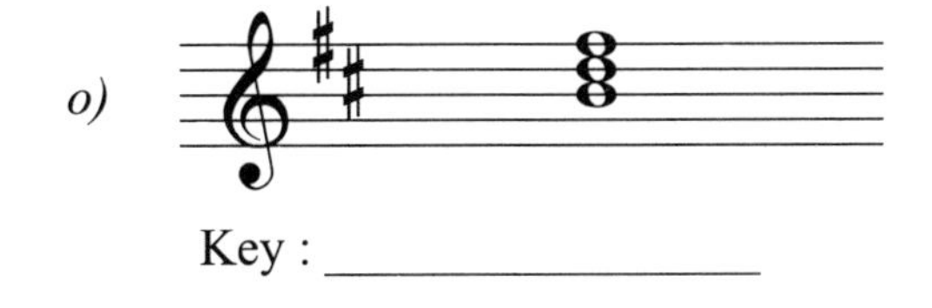

Key : ________________

p) 

Key : ________________

7. Write the following scales, using the given rhythms. Add any necessary accidentals:

a)

C melodic minor, ascending, with key signature

b)

F♯ harmonic minor, descending, with key signature

c)

A♭ major, ascending, with key signature

d)

F melodic minor, ascending, without key signature

e)

E major, descending, without key signature

Intervals

An interval can be described not just by its number, but also by its quality.

For example, starting on the key-note of C, the possibilities are:

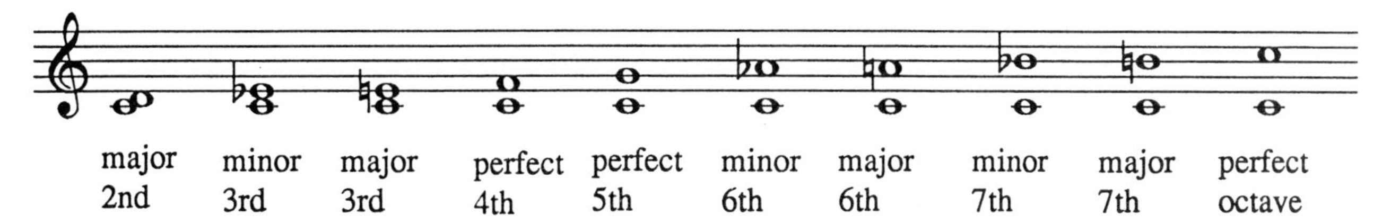

Each interval thus contains a fixed number of semitones:

Interval	No. of Semitones
Major 2nd	2
(Minor 3rd)	3
Major 3rd	4
Perfect 4th	5
Perfect 5th	7
(Minor 6th)	8
Major 6th	9
(Minor 7th)	10
Major 7th	11
Perfect 8ve	12

You may use either of these methods to determine the quality of a given interval:

i) Count the number of semitones between the two notes and the full interval can then be determined:

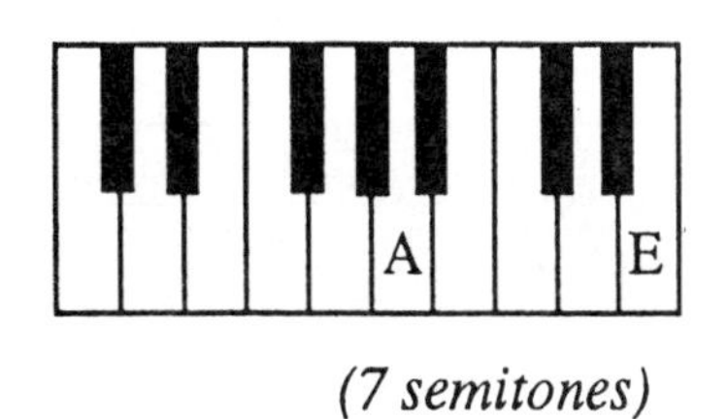

(7 semitones)

ii) The other alternative method is to count the size of the interval, i.e. up the scale from the key-note:

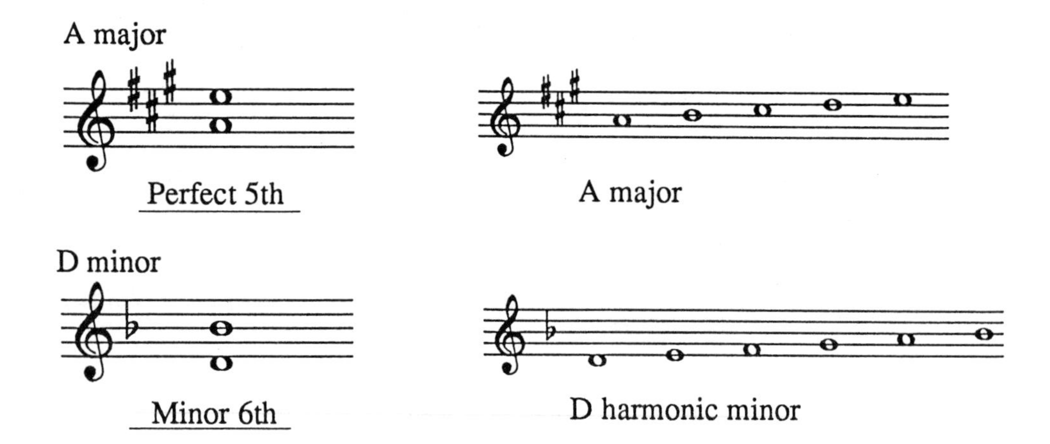

1. Write the full name of the following intervals (e.g. major 6th, perfect 8ve etc.):

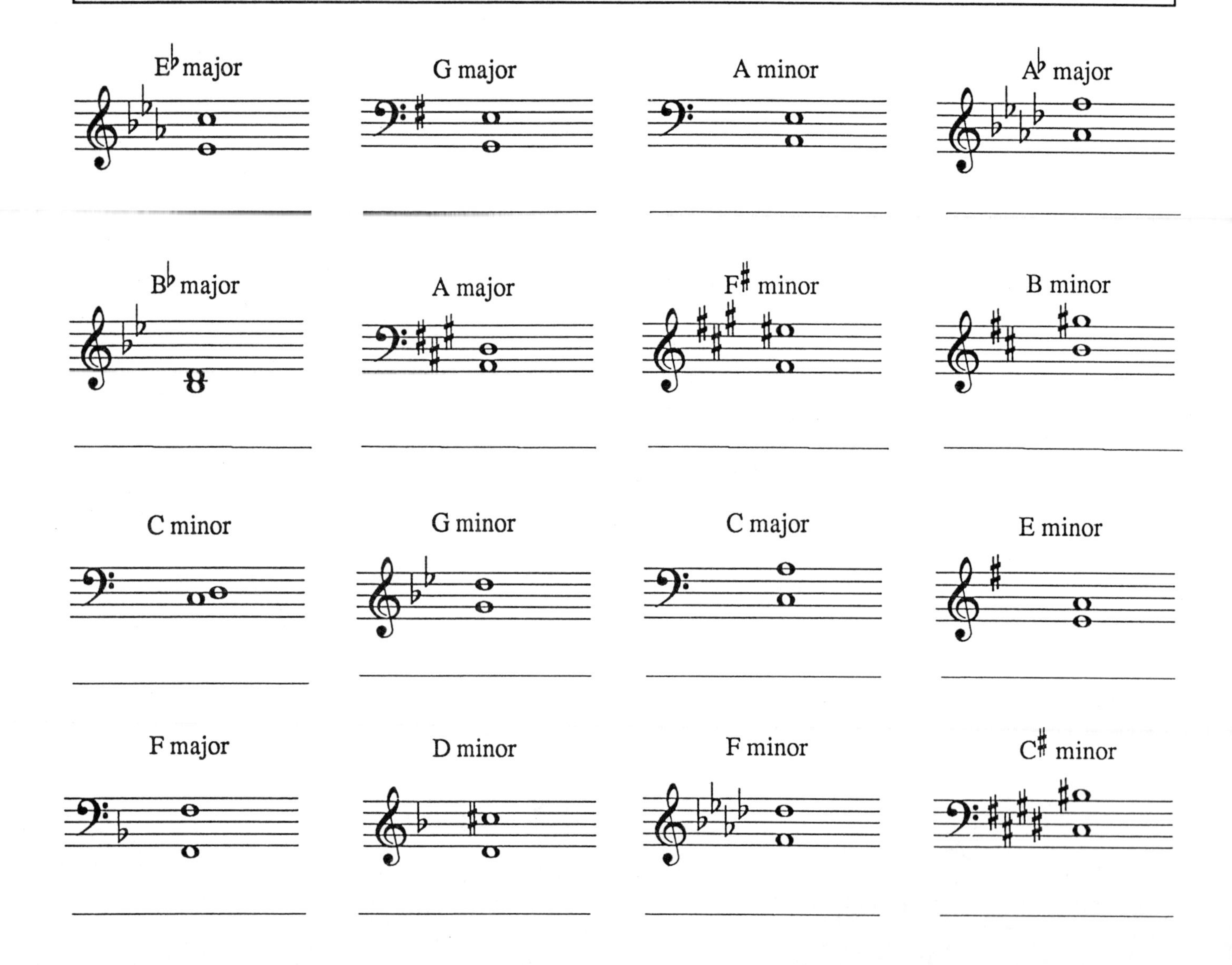

2. Write a note above the given note in each of the following so as to form the interval named. The key has been named in each:

Working: Count 8 semitones from C. The note reached is A♭. (It must not be written enharmonically as G♯ due to the interval of a 6th.)

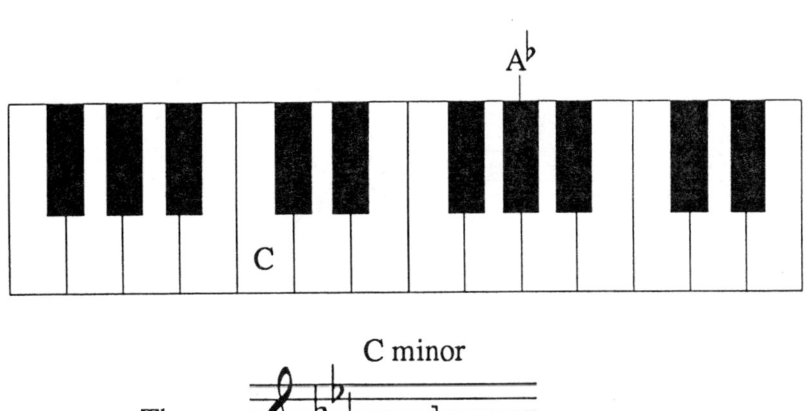

Thus:

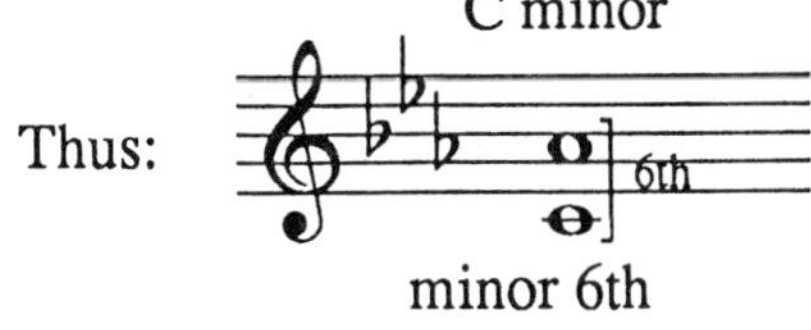

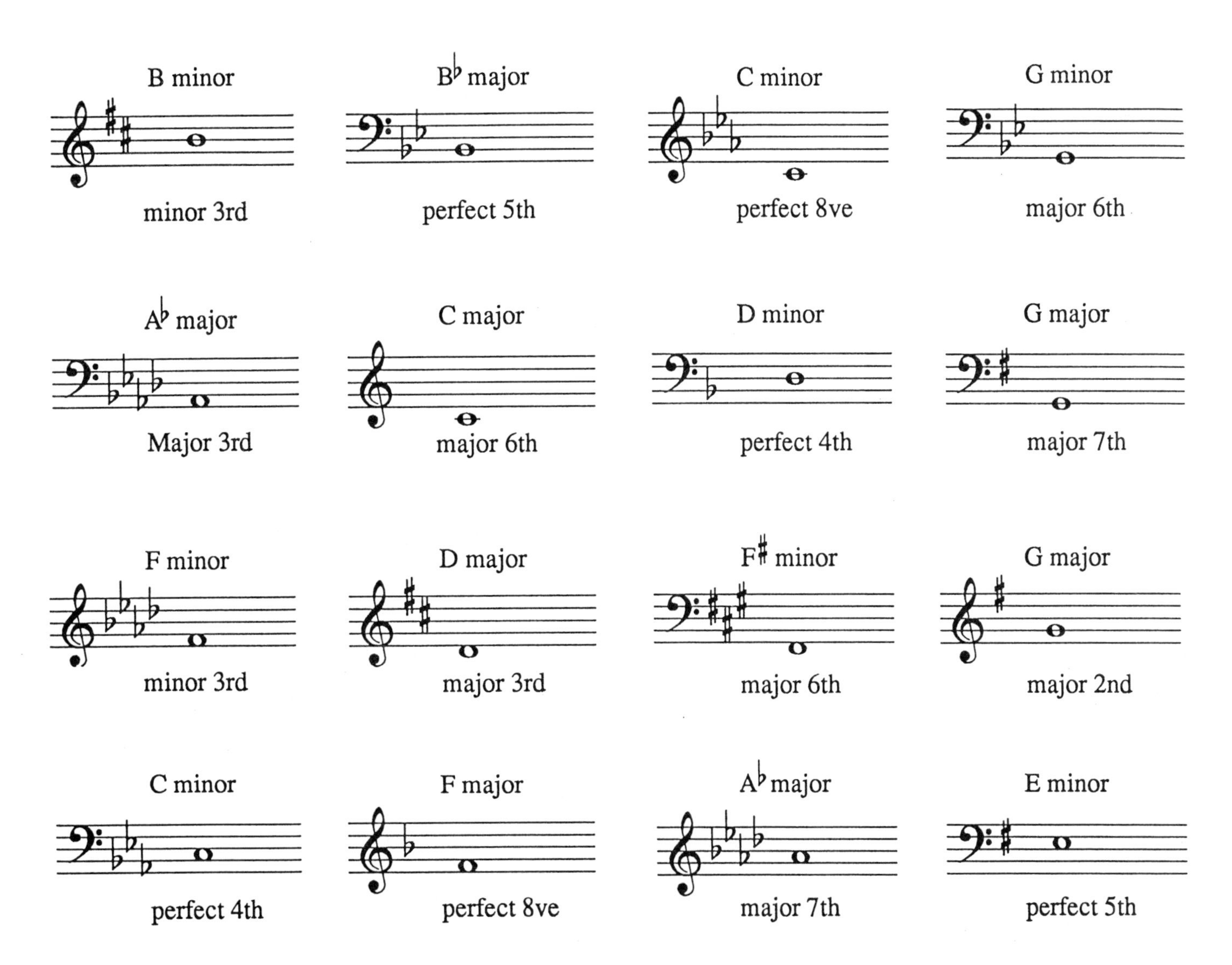

3. Write a note above each of these notes so as to form the interval named. Do not use any key signature (Notice that the key has not been given.):

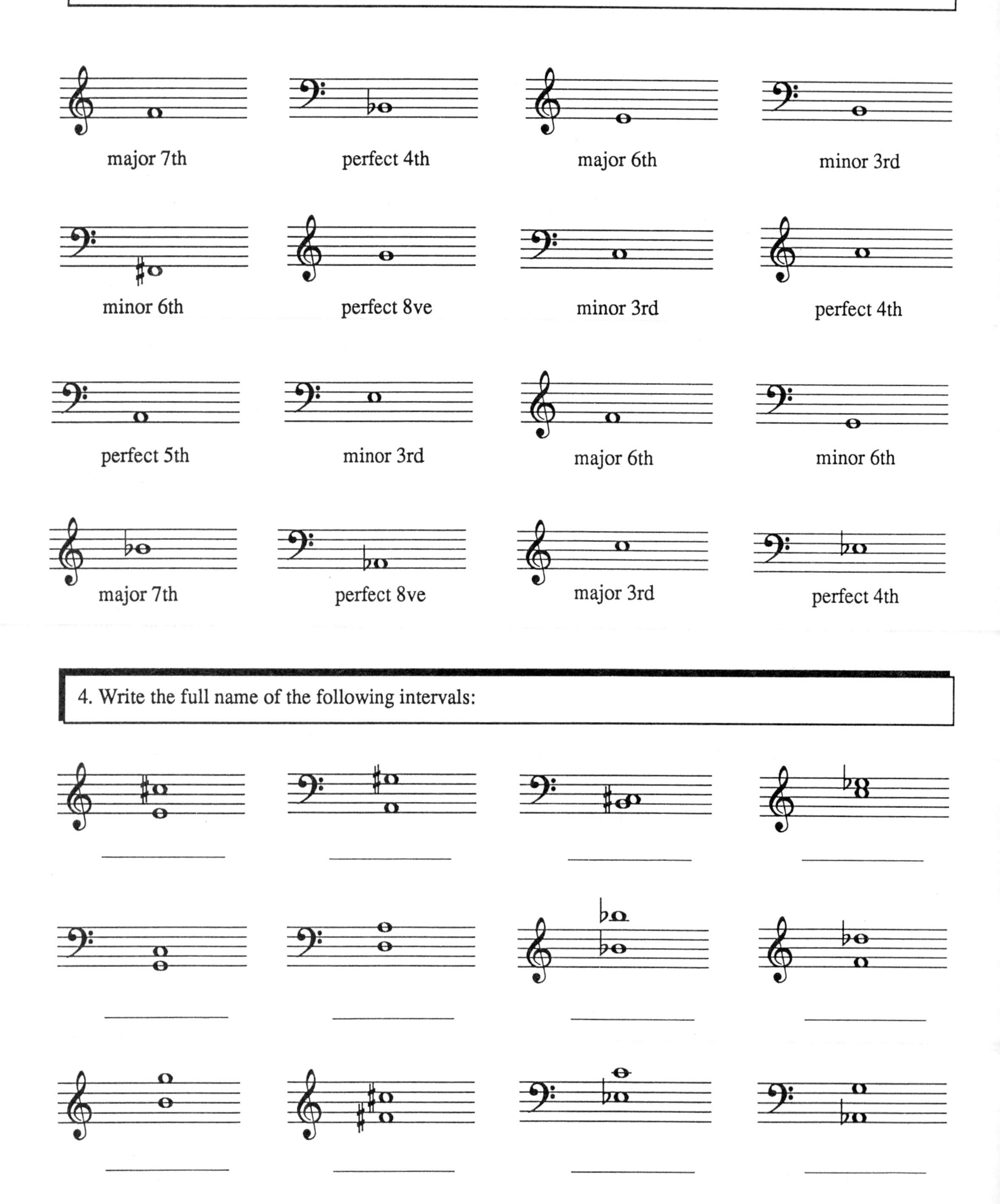

5. Name the interval between each pair of notes marked with a ⌐¬ . The lower note is the key-note of the melody:

a) Couperin, La Commere

1. ______________ 2. ______________ 3. ______________

b)

1. ______________ 2. ______________

c) J.S. Bach, Fugue in F♯ (from the '48', Bk.2)

1. ______________ 2. ______________

d) Franck, 3 Chorales

1. ______________ 2. ______________

e) Liszt, Au Lac De Wallenstadt

1. ______________ 2. ______________

f) Purcell, Fairy Queen

1. ______________ 2. ______________ 3. ______________

g) J.S. Bach, Concerto No.3 in C minor

1. ______________ 2. ______________

Four-bar Rhythms

A four-bar rhythmic phrase may start "off-beat", called an ***anacrusis***.

For example:

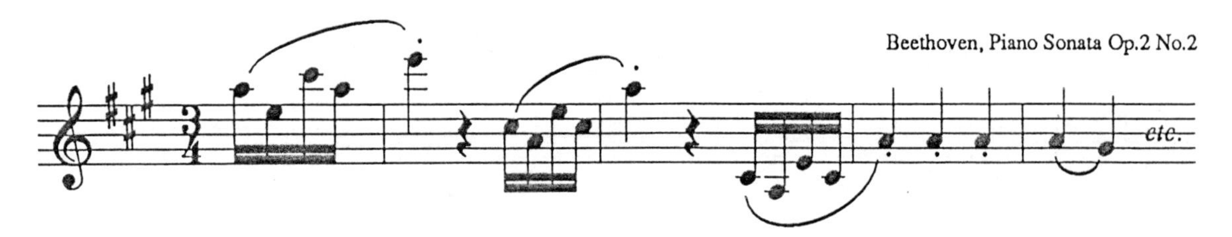

A phrase which starts before the first bar often ends with the number of beats, which, when added to those before the first bar, adds up to a complete bar.

Most four-bar rhythms contain some repetitions,

For example:

'A' is repeated 3 times.

The first half is repeated.

The opening figure is repeated in the 2nd half.

The opening figure is repeated immediately.

Some rhythms may contain no repetitions at all, but care must be taken not to use too many different types of note values:

This is good:

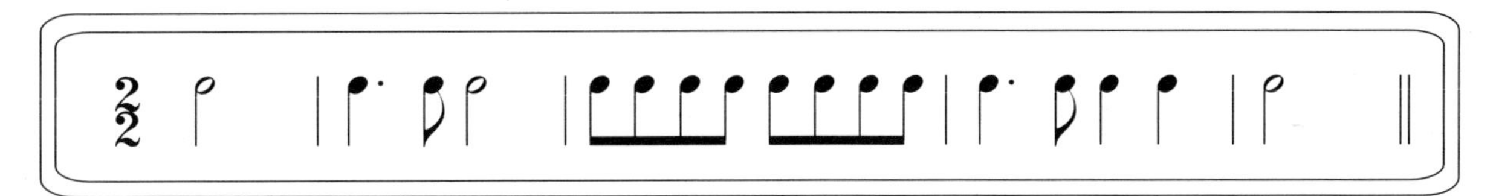

1. Compose four-bar rhythms based on these openings. Use repetitions and indicate them by using a ⌐¬ :

a)

b)

c)

d)

e)

f)

g)

h)

2. Compose four-bar rhythms from these openings. Do not use any repetitions:

d)

3. Write four-bar rhythms in each of the given time signatures below. Include the given rhythms, though not necessarily at the beginning:

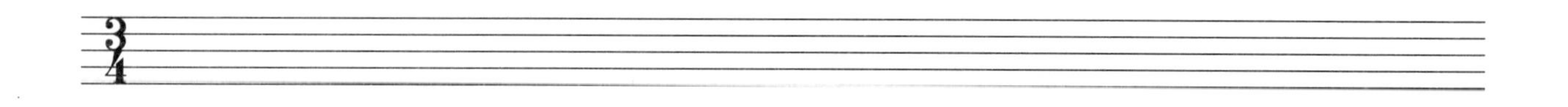

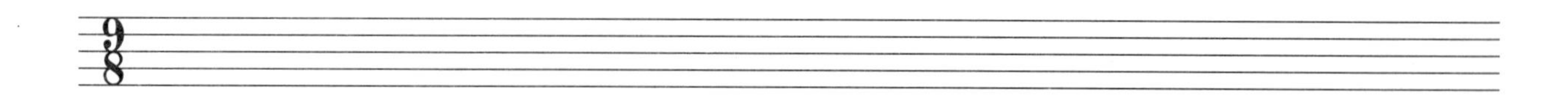

c) Use and

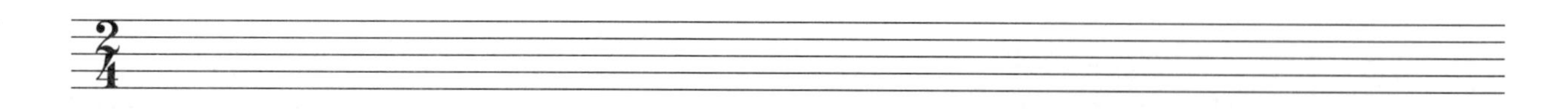

d) Use and
e) Use and
f) Use and
3
g) Use and
h) Use and
3
i) Use and

Simple Phrase Structures

A melody can be divided into parts, called phrases. In grade 3, the phrases are mostly two or four bars long. Sometimes three bar phrases also occur, though they are less common.

Here is an example:

To determine the length of phrases:

i) A rhythmic pattern may be repeated or the phrases may begin with the same rhythm. (as in the above example)

ii) Long notes are sometimes used at phrase ends, such as:

iii) If words are set to music, the phrases normally follow the pauses in speech rhythm:

1. Mark each phrase with a ⌐¬ to show the phrase-structure in each of the melodies:

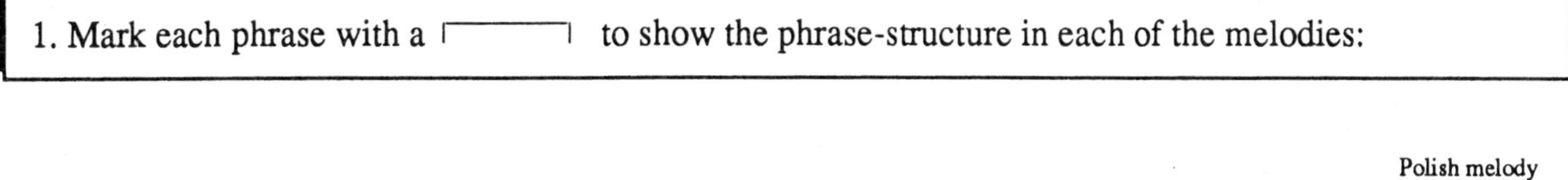

Americian Ballad: The Streets of Laredo

Camidge, Piano Sonata No.1 in G

Bach, Gavotte II from English Suite No.3

The Lincolnshire Poacher
f)
Chopin, Mazurka in G minor
g)
Mozart, The Magic Flute

Musical Terms

Apart from the terms and signs in Grades 1 and 2, the student is supposed to know the following terms. Explain them:

1. On Tempo

Alla breve ____________________

Adagietto ____________________

Ad libitum, ad lib. ____________________

Rubato, tempo rubato ____________________

Stringendo ____________________

2. On Performance Direction

Agitato ____________________

Amore ____________________

Amoroso ____________________

Anima ____________________

Animando ____________________

Brio ____________________

Deciso ____________________

Delicato ____________________

Energico ____________________

Largamente ____________________

Leggiero ____________________

Marcato, marc. ______________________

Marziale ______________________

Mesto ______________________

Pesante ______________________

Risoluto ______________________

Ritmico ______________________

Scherzando, scherzoso ______________________

Semplice ______________________

Tranquillo ______________________

Triste ______________________

3. Other Terms

These terms are often combined with another:

Ben ______________________
Ben marcato ______________________

Prima, primo ______________________
Tempo primo ______________________

Seconda, secondo ______________________
Seconda volta ______________________

Sempre ______________________
Sempre ***f*** ______________________

Subito ______________________
Subito ***p*** ______________________

Tanto ______________________
Allegro non tanto ______________________

Volta ______________________
Prima volta ______________________

General Exercises

1. This melody is played by the violins at the opening of the second movement of Beethoven's 3rd Symphony. Look at it and asnwer the questions below.

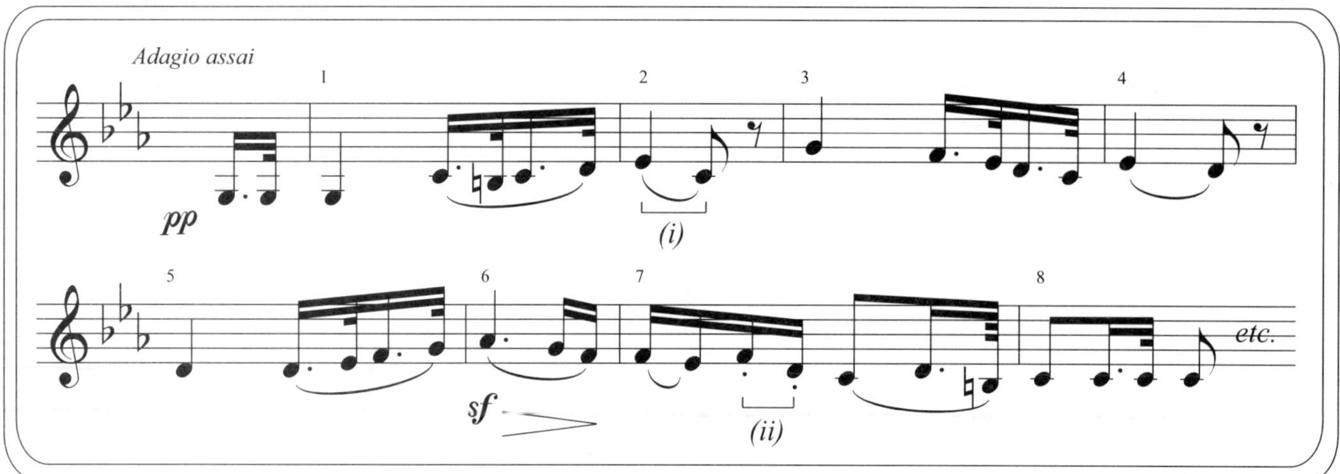

a) What is the key of the passage? ______________________

b) Name another key which has the same key signature. ______________________

c) Add the time signature where required.

d) One bar contains all the notes of the tonic triad. It is bar ______

e) Name the intervals marked (i) and (ii).

(i) ______________________ (ii) ______________________

f) What is the time name of the shortest note? ______________________

g) Give the meaning of the following:

Adagio assai ______________________

sf (bar 6) ______________________

(bar 5) ______________________

(in bar 2) ______________________

h) Rewrite the passage from bar 5 to bar 8. Do not use a key signature but add any necessary accidentals. Include the time signature.

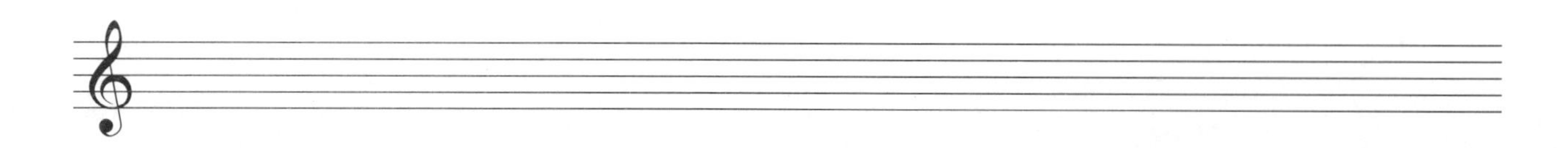

2. This is a violin melody from Beethoven's Piano Quartet in E♭ major Op.16. Look at it and then answer the questions below:

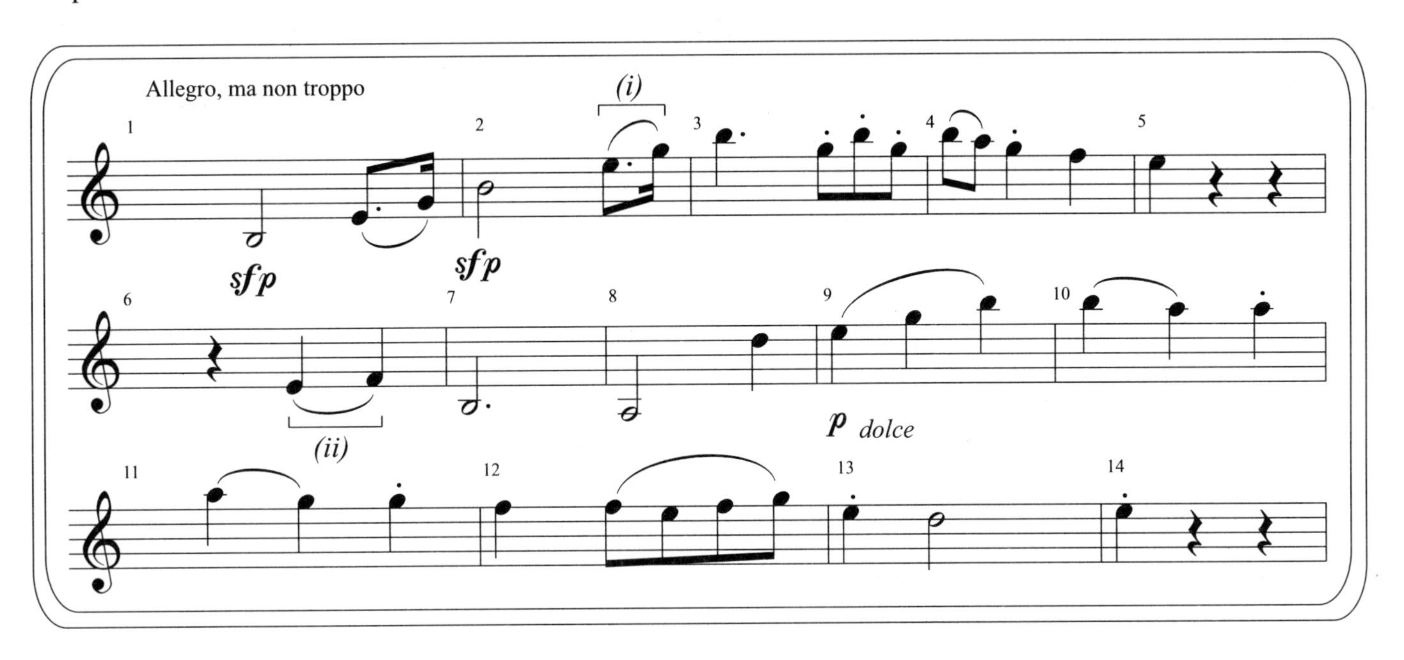

a) The passage is in E♭ major. Add the key signature at the approriate places.

b) Write the correct time signature at the beginning of the extract. What kind of time is it?

(Simple or compound; duple, triple etc.) ____

c) Which two bars contain all the notes of the tonic triad? Bar ______and bar ______.

d) Circle the 4th degree of the scale which occurs between bars 1 and 5.

e) Name the lowest note. It is ____in bar _____ .

f) Give the meaning of the following:

Allegro ma non troppo ________________________________

dolce ________________________________

sfp ________________________________

dots above notes in bar 3 ________________________________

g) Name the intervals marked *(i)* and *(ii)*

(i) ____________________ *(ii)* ____________________

h) Rewrite bars 1 to 5 in notes of double the value. Include the new time signature.

3. This is a melody from Haydn's String quartets. Look at it and then answer the questions that follow:

a) What does *Allegro* mean? ____________________________________

b) In what key is the first five bars of the music? ____________________________________

c) Describe the time (simple or compund; duple etc.). ____________________________________

d) In which bars do the highest notes appear? In bars ________ and ________ .

e) How many times does the rhythms ♩ ♪ appear? ________________________

f) Which bar has the most number of notes? Bar _______

Why is it so? ____

g) There is a tied note at bar ______________

h) The melody leaps an octave at two places: bar ______ and bar _______ .

i) Complete bars 5 and 11 with the correct rest or rests.

j) Underline one of the metronome marks which would be suitable for the passage.

♩ = 100 ♩. = 100 ♪ = 100 𝅗𝅥 = 100

k) Transpose the first 5 bars (as far as the note marked *) down an octave. Use the bass clef.

Specimen Test

Total Marks 100

1. Add the correct time signature to each of the following:

10

2 Rewrite the following notes, grouping them correctly into a) $\frac{3}{2}$ time; b) $\frac{12}{8}$ time. Start on the first beat of the bar and then fill in each of the last bars with a rest or rests:

10

a) $\frac{3}{2}$

b) $\frac{12}{8}$

3. Write the correct clef and key signature of each of the following. You may use any necessary accidentals:

10

a)

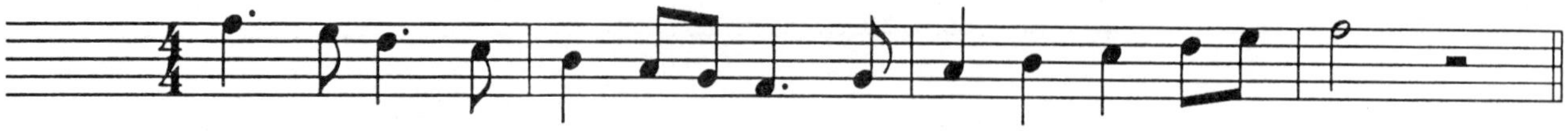

F♯ harmonic minor

b)

C harmonic minor

4. Describe the intervals below. The key is D minor:

10

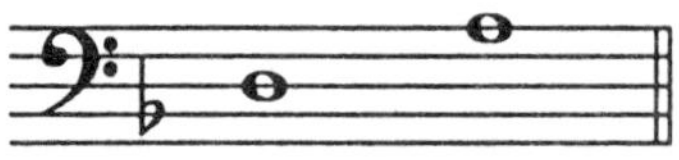

______________ ______________ ______________

______________ ______________

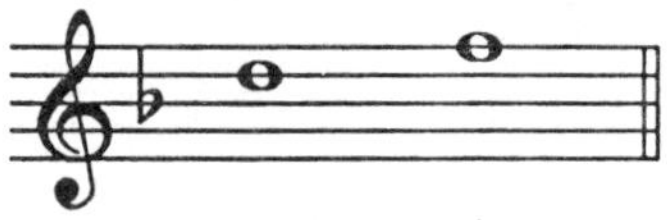

5. Name the key of each of the following tonic triads:

10

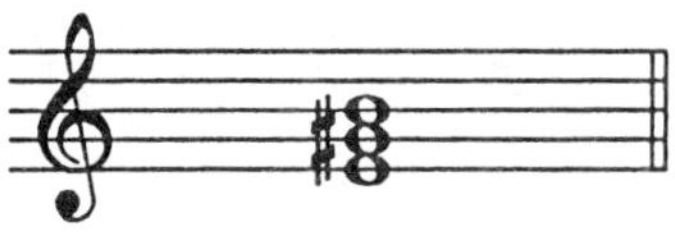

______________ ______________ ______________

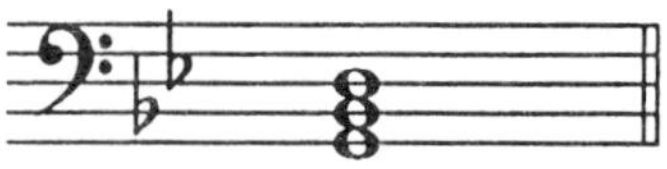

______________ ______________

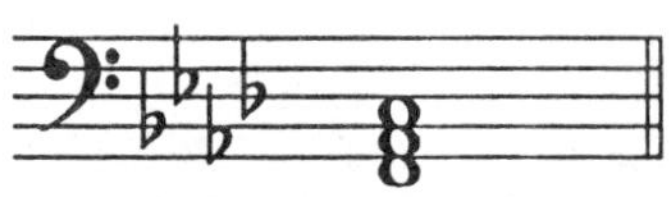

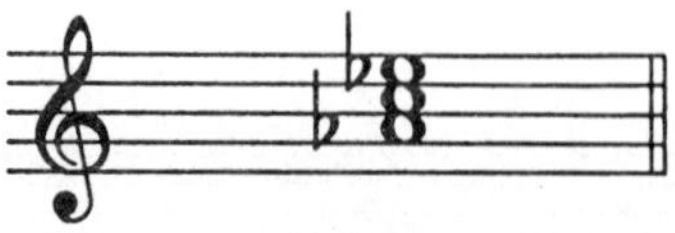

6. Transpose this given melody up an octave into the treble clef:

10

7. This is the opening melody of Kabelevsky's Sonatina Op.13 No.2 (2nd movt.). Look at it and then answer the questions that follow:

10

a) i) Is the melody in simple or compound time? ______________________

ii) Write the beats (e.g. 1,2,3) in their correct places underneath the notes of bars 6 and 7.

iii) How many times does the rhythm ♪. ♬ occur? ______________

iv) For how long does the longest note last? __________ crotchet beats.

10

b) *i)* The first phrase has been marked ⌐¬. Mark in the same way where it is repeated.

ii) Explain the following terms:

sostenuto (at the beginning) ______________________________

crescendo (bar 6) __________________________

iii) Which is the highest note? At which bar is it found? __________ at bar __________.

iv) Circle two notes which form the interval of a minor 3rd.

10

c) Transpose the melody from the beginning to the place marked * an octave lower. Use the bass clef. Insert the correct key signature.

8. Write a four-bar rhythm using the given time signature, beginning as shown:

10